THE PURSUIT OF THE ATOM

The original German edition was
published in Stuttgart, under the title
Förscher erschüttern die Welt. This
English translation is published in London
as *The Drama of the Atom.*

THE PURSUIT OF
THE ATOM

BY

WERNER BRAUNBEK

TRANSLATED BY

BRIAN J. KENWORTHY

AND

W. A. COUPE

EMERSON BOOKS, INC.
NEW YORK

S
539/14
B82

QC
7
B673

38600

JAN 13 1960

CONTENTS

FOREWORD

Most forewords go unread; perhaps the obvious shortness of this one may save it from such a fate. All that matters is in the book itself, and does not need to be set forth in a foreword. Nevertheless, I should like to draw the reader's attention to two points.

I cannot claim for my book the formula that is so popular nowadays: 'all characters and incidents in this book are fictitious; any resemblance to people living or dead is purely accidental.' Quite the reverse—I have been at pains to follow as closely as possible the events as they really happened. And these have an inherent dramatic quality which entitles them to speak for themselves. On the other hand, the book is not intended to document the history of science, and so I would beg the forbearance of those concerned for any small divergence from the historical facts.

Others whose forbearance I must also seek for omitting a list of my sources are those very many authors of scientific and non-scientific works upon which I have drawn in writing this book. In any case, no one will doubt that a book of this sort could not be written without the reading of innumerable other books, scientific works, etc.

Finally, I ask the indulgence of my readers if here and there a sentence, an idea, an expression should not be understood. The general impression will not suffer thereby. For my book is not intended as a text-book, nor even as a book of instruction, but as the surging symphony of an epoch without precedent.

TRANSLATORS' NOTE

The number terminology in this book follows German-British usage
French-American equivalents are given below

MILLIARD herein = the French-American BILLION

BILLION herein = the French-American TRILLION

TRILLION herein = the French-American QUINTILLION

etc.

1

A MAN NAMED RUTHERFORD

M ONDAY, 25th October 1937. The typical autumn fog of
London hangs in the damp streets of the great city.
Although it is midday, the light is gloomy; and it would
be quite dark inside the 700-year-old walls of Westminster
Abbey, in the lofty Gothic nave, were it not for the reddish light
shed by the six-branched candelabra on each of the pillars that
disappear into the darkness above.

Their light falls upon a distinguished group of mourners.
Lord sits next to lord in the carved pews. Lord Fortescue is
representing King George VI, who has not yet been a year on the
throne since the sensational abdication of Edward VIII. Beside
him are Lord Halifax, Lord Swinton, Lord Chatfield, and then
the former Prime Ministers Earl Baldwin and Ramsay Mac-
donald (who is destined to die a fortnight later on a trip to South
America), and next the Home Secretary Sir Samuel Hoare—all
people who were prominent in the affairs of Britain before the
war.

One might have thought that this last tribute, ending now in
solemn silence with the dying organ chords after the anthem:
'I am the resurrection and the life . . .' had been paid to a great
politician, a famous shaper of the destinies of the century. But
this time it is not a statesman. The man whose ashes lie in the
urn which is being carried with slow step through the nave and
choir of Westminster Abbey was a man of science, a man of pure
research: he was the Right Honourable Ernest, First Baron
Rutherford, Lord of Nelson, New Zealand, and Cambridge.

This Ernest Rutherford was not even an Englishman in the
strict sense, as were the illustrious scientists who already rest

here—Newton, Kelvin, Darwin, scholars whose silent company he will now join. Ernest Rutherford, more than almost any other scientist, was a man of the world-wide Empire: he had been born sixty-six years before in the little town of Brightwater near Nelson in New Zealand, where he grew up; for nine years he was at McGill University in Montreal in Canada, and only then, already famous, though still a young man, had he come to live in England. Can these lords, ministers, politicians, whose minds must be preoccupied with very different matters in this tense atmosphere of less than two years before the outbreak of the war against Hitler's Germany—can they have even a partial comprehension of the achievements of this great man, past whose urn they are now filing, before it is covered by the marble slab bearing his name? One thing is certain: not one of them suspects—or indeed can suspect—that in less than a decade the discoveries made by Ernest Rutherford will have become a political consideration of an importance never attained by any other scientific discovery, that from them a glittering promise and diabolical terror will reach out to the very ends of our earth.

Now that the complete silence is broken by the shuffle of many feet, two men are whispering in the back rows:

'Who was this Lord Rutherford?'

'He discovered the nucleus,' answers the other, adding with a shudder: 'He had actually split atoms.' He is obviously well-informed, at least superficially. It does not mean very much to the questioner, but he lets it rest. The word goes echoing away: nucleus.

The nucleus—a star that has risen in the firmament of modern physics, too bright to be overlooked or neglected—but as yet only for the scientists. The great majority of people do not yet know this word nucleus or its meaning. So far it has remained within the confines of scientific research; no one yet knows its promises of inexhaustible industrial energy, or of its diabolical threat of death and destruction. But the idea is there—living, developing, growing. And here, now, the man whose experiments and thought created the new conception, called the new idea into being, has just been lowered into the grave: Ernest Rutherford.

*　　　*　　　*

A man who comes into the world as the fourth of the twelve children of an artisan in modest circumstances has no obvious or immediate prospect of obtaining many of the goods of this world. Moreover, a wretched little place like Spring Grove—to-day called Brightwater—a dozen miles south of the insignificant port of Nelson on the South Island of New Zealand, is not the best starting-point for a great career. Fate had bestowed only one favour on this humble man by the name of Rutherford: that he should have been born into a time so eminently propitious to his development.

Let us look at the world as it appeared on 30th August 1871, the day on which Ernest Rutherford began to breathe the air of New Zealand. Six months earlier Germany and France had concluded with the Peace of Frankfurt the short but significant war—for upon it had followed the unification of the German Empire under Bismarck—and both could now apply themselves peacefully and constructively to their industrial progress. England, Victorian England, was already blazing the trail of industrialization. The United States, whose bloody civil war had ended six years before, were catching up with giant strides. And so a wave of rising prosperity ran round the world, fostering the development of science and research. These, again, were also in great demand with the young and rapidly growing industry, which in turn played a decisive part in their fruitful advance. In the atmosphere thus engendered science was welcomed, and welcomed enthusiastically. Formerly art and literature had held the cultural field; now they were joined by the sciences as a new element of general interest, and foremost among them were the exact sciences: chemistry and physics.

Around the turn of the century came a series of the most remarkable scientific discoveries: in 1887 Hertz was experimenting with electrical waves, and in 1895 Marconi developed from them wireless telegraphy; in the same year Röntgen discovered X-rays, and in 1896 Becquerel discovered radio-activity; in 1897 the free electron was discovered by J. J. Thomson, and in 1898 the Curies found radium. In 1900 the quantum theory was established by Planck, and in 1905 the theory of relativity by Einstein. How fortunate for a man of Rutherford's stature to be at the height of his powers at a time like this!

But as yet Rutherford, who has moved to the neighbouring town of Foxhill, is still a small boy who goes to school and plays like any other boy. Neither is there anything outstanding about the youth of fifteen who gains a scholarship to Nelson College.

One thing stands out, however: at school he was always above the average—he passed the examination which won him the sorely needed scholarship with 580 out of a possible 600 marks. Some maintain that good pupils seldom make great men, but Rutherford is a striking example of the opposite—and there are many more. He was a gifted boy, and at the age of ten his interest was aroused by a physics text-book that came into his possession—and he never lost his interest in physics.

So in the following years it was not difficult for him to win scholarships for a scientific education. At eighteen he went to the University of New Zealand at Canterbury College in Christchurch, and at twenty-two took his M.A. in mathematics and physics.

During the next year he was engaged in research on the waves discovered by Hertz, on the magnetization of iron through high-frequency discharges, which enable him to construct a new and sensitive detector for electrical waves. And then comes his big chance: Ernest Rutherford wins a scholarship that will take him to England! He is digging potatoes when the happy news reaches him. Throwing the spade aside, he leaps up and says: 'That's the last potato I'll ever dig!'

So we see in August 1895 a young man of twenty-four named Rutherford setting out with borrowed money, leaving his native land, to which his Scottish grandfather had emigrated half a century before; we see him hastening to those far shores with youth's eternal dream of fortune and success in his heart.

*   *   *

Nevertheless young Rutherford's feelings are divided as he stands on the deck of the boat that for days has been ploughing through the Indian Ocean. The scientist longs to reach the British homeland, where he rightly expects to work with famous men in a very different, more stimulating scientific climate than that offered by the remote colonial territory. But the man is still drawn to the island he knows, with its imposing, wild landscape. His heart belongs to a girl there, to Mary Newton, the daughter of his landlady in Christchurch, the *filia hospitalis* of his early student days.

Now she must remain behind, but he will come back for her. And five years will pass until his position is secure—yet he fears no inconstancy of his heart. Ernest Rutherford is as straightforward and unequivocal in love as he is in his scientific work. In love at nineteen, engaged at twenty-four, married at twenty-nine—and, of course, it is always the same girl, Mary, who will remain loyally with him until his death.

His thoughts turn to the future. Soon Rutherford will be in England, after travelling half-way round the world—in London, and soon at the great University of Cambridge. Here he will be lucky enough to work in the Cavendish, England's most famous laboratory: the Cavendish, which, since its foundation in 1874, has been directed by such men as Maxwell and Lord Rayleigh and is now under Professor Joseph John Thomson, known to his students simply as 'J.J.' Although he is scarcely forty, he has already made his name with his work on the passing of electricity through gases, in the course of which he was shortly afterwards to discover free electrons.

And then he is in the presence of the great man, by whom he is warmly received and at once made to feel at home. As he entered the renowned laboratory, could he have suspected that in twenty-four years he would himself be returning as its director? It does not take Rutherford long to accustom himself to his new surroundings; even if he and his fellow research student, J. S. E. Townsend, later a professor at Oxford University, were at first accepted with some reserve by a few of the old laboratory assistants, it was not long before he had won general esteem.

Rutherford did not come to Cambridge empty-handed. In Christchurch he had already established his scientific career with his invention of the detector for electrical waves. In Cambridge he continues his work on these problems. He is the first man in England—even before Marconi's celebrated experiments—to transmit wireless signals through the walls of several rooms, and eventually a distance of about a mile. Rutherford might easily have devoted himself entirely to this work; and that might have added to the history of communications the name of yet another distinguished radio engineer. But modern physics would have lost the man who pursued an idea so persistently that around his work crystallized that of a whole generation of research workers. We have to thank the Cavendish laboratory, Rutherford's own bent, and his supervisor J. J. Thomson for the fact that he gradually moved ever further towards pure research, into the world of electrons, ions, and radiation.

During the three years that Rutherford was doing research at the Cavendish, two discoveries were made which astonished the scientific world. In 1895, the year in which Rutherford came to England, and less than two months after his arrival at the Cavendish, an obscure German professor, Röntgen, in Würzburg discovered some very strange rays that penetrate matter, and which he could produce at will by passing a sufficiently high electric current through a discharge tube. And the following year Becquerel in Paris discovered radio-activity, by observing that uranium compounds spontaneously give out a continual penetrating radiation, like X-rays—though later it proved to be much more complex. At the Cavendish, 'J.J.' immediately seized upon both discoveries, and worked with X-rays and uranium radiation, which enabled him to produce 'ions' in air, that is, electrically charged molecules of oxygen or nitrogen from the air. Rutherford comes into close contact with these things, makes his own experiments, and is captivated by the mystery of this new world: he has found the dominant interest of his life.

Since a research student has little prospect of promotion, he nevertheless wishes to leave the Cavendish; for he wants to settle down and marry. And so he applies for, and is elected to, a vacant professorship at the Canadian McGill University in Montreal. On 8th September 1898 Ernest Rutherford boards the *Yorkshire*, which carries him still further westwards across the Atlantic. The little 5,000 ton steamer can fight its way only very slowly through the autumn gales, once out of the shelter of the Irish coast.

Again Rutherford looks into the future. His thoughts turn upon his new post, now that he is no longer a student, but a **professor** earning some £500 a year. His mind is filled with plans for the years of hard work ahead, which are to lead him to the first peak of his career.

*   *   *

The industrial port of Montreal with its two universities lies on an island in the St. Lawrence. McGill is the older university. A Canadian millionaire, McDonald, is the principal patron of the university; though he made his money in tobacco, he abhors the tobacco habit himself. Indeed, all traces of smoking must disappear whenever the benefactor visits its departments. In other ways, too, he is eccentric: in spite of his wealth he lives on something like £500 a year; from which, of course, the university benefits.

And so in the late autumn of 1898 Ernest Rutherford sets to work in the physics department here, whose previous director was a mathematician. Hence there is little provision for experimental work, so that he has to groom it to suit his purposes. For he has brought with him the legacy of his research in the Cavendish: the whole field which he has made his own under J. J. Thomson—ions in gases, the radiation they produce, and particularly the mysterious radiation of uranium, which unceasingly fascinates him. And here is the place to realize all those plans which are urging themselves upon him.

In Cambridge Rutherford had already worked with uranium and thorium, that other element which similarly emits these puzzling rays. He had already established that these rays are not uniform, but are of two distinct types which he called alpha and beta rays.

Incidentally, Paul Villard had, in 1900, discovered a new group—gamma rays. These proved to be closely related to X-rays, were extremely penetrating and were not deflected by a magnetic field. Beta rays were electrons travelling at almost the speed of light, were easily deflected and could only penetrate thin sheets of metal. Alpha rays, however, clearly also particles of matter travelling at high speed—later to become famous as alpha particles—but less penetrating than beta rays and deflectable to a certain extent, presented the immediate great mystery and became the object of Rutherford's life-long researches.

During the first years in Montreal, however, he must follow

other paths. New to his professorship and regardless of the pressure of other work, he immediately initiates an extensive research programme. One of his students, R. B. Owens, entrusted with an examination of thorium radiation, runs into peculiar difficulties, and in the course of his studies discovers thorium emanation, the first of those three strange radio-active gases to be discovered, which emanate from thorium, radium, and actinium.

In thorium emanation Rutherford meets for the first time a radio-active substance, whose radiation does not remain constant, but diminishes rapidly. Here Rutherford discovers the basic law which governs the rate of this diminution, a law which proves to be universally valid for all radio-active materials, and which could not be observed in the case of radium and thorium, since the process in these materials is much too slow to permit direct observation. Thus, light begins slowly to penetrate the dark mystery of radio-activity.

With the hesitant dawning of this new light, to the increase of which Rutherford and his band of followers fanatically devote themselves, we pass into the next century. In Paris, the lights of the World Exhibition proclaim the perfection of technology and the Machine Age. Self-satisfaction is the basic mood of the masses and even in scientific circles the opinion that man will soon have reached the limits of all knowledge is prevalent. Years previously a friend had asked Rutherford how he could be a physicist, when the field was obviously practically exhausted. To-day we smile at this opinion, passed at the very moment when physics was entering its most startling period of discovery.

In Montreal work proceeds smoothly and now at last Rutherford can enjoy a short holiday. He goes to New Zealand and returns with his bride, Mary, whom he had left behind five years previously, in order to make his way in the world. His efforts have been crowned with success, and when, in the autumn of 1900, Rutherford sets up home with his young wife in Montreal, he feels that he has achieved an initial measure of security. But Ernest Rutherford sets to work again: the lure of the undiscovered outweighs any desire for a life of unruffled domesticity.

*   *   *

At about this time, Frederick Soddy, a very capable and ambitious young chemist from Oxford, arrives at McGill. Since Rutherford's work often touches on chemical problems (e.g. the nature of new substances produced, such as the thorium emanation) he needs the help of a chemist, and so, for three fruitful years, Rutherford and Soddy work together.

First of all, they discover that the gas-like thorium emanation is not produced directly from thorium, but indirectly from a new substance, which they call thorium-X, itself a thorium product. When the properties of the new substance are examined it is found that the latter is completely different from thorium (to-day we know that it is an 'isotope' of radium) and may be separated from it chemically. But the most amazing discovery is that if thorium-X is completely separated from thorium, the thorium-X is gradually replaced at exactly the same rate at which the separated thorium-X would disappear as it was transformed into thorium emanation. (The time-curves of the increasing and diminishing thorium-X reappeared later in Rutherford's coat of arms when he was elevated to the peerage.)

To-day we know that thorium-X is not produced directly from thorium and that there are no less than three intermediate stages between the two, all of which were later discovered by Otto Hahn. What was then known, however, was remarkable enough. From thorium arises thorium-X, from thorium-X thorium emanation; and it became increasingly clear that all three substances were chemical elements.

The sudden and illuminating discovery was summarized by Rutherford and Soddy in their famous theory of radio-active decay. Radio-active elements change, as a result of radiation, into other chemical elements, most of which are themselves radio-active and in turn change into yet other elements.

When articles on the theory of radio-active decay appeared in the *Philosophical Magazine* in London in September and November 1902, the scientific world was shaken to its foundations. The theory had established Rutherford's fame and met with passionate support and passionate opposition.

For many years to come the theory remained a bone of contention. It must be emphasized how heretical the idea was for those times, signifying, as it did, the destruction of the concept of chemical elements. The chemists defined an element as a substance which could under no circumstances be changed into a different element, in contrast to a chemical compound, built up of elements, into which it could be broken down. Finally, however, the theory of radio-active decay remained victorious; there was no gainsaying the weight of the experimental proofs.

The next years bring ever more work. Rutherford turns his attention to alpha rays and succeeds in deflecting them electrically and magnetically. Soddy tells the amusing story of how Rutherford one day touched some apparatus without having switched off the current and danced about the room, swearing like a trooper and in his anger smashing the carefully constructed apparatus on the floor.

Rutherford measures the speed of alpha rays—12,500 miles per second—much less than that of the electrons of beta rays but a terribly high speed, when one considers the relatively great size of the particles, and he estimates by measuring the electric charge the number of particles emitted by radio-active materials: 1 gm. of radium he estimates as producing almost 100 milliards (the later, exact assessment was 36·8 milliards). Even then Rutherford suspects that the alpha particles are ionized atoms of helium (i.e. atoms with a positive electric charge). Step by step, this bold conjecture is proved to be correct. In 1903, Ramsay and Soddy prove that helium is constantly being produced from radium, and in 1908 Rutherford—already by this time professor in Manchester—obtains positive proof that it is the alpha particles which make up helium, since they themselves consist of helium.

Tirelessly Rutherford works on. He discovers the first links in the radio-active chain of radium; he measures the mysterious increase in temperature taking place in radio-active materials and calculates the enormous energy which they liberate. In a lecture in St. Louis as early as 1903 he tells his astounded audience that if one could produce a pound of emanation—in experiments only fractions of a milligramme were used—it would continuously produce the equivalent of 10,000 horse power.

In 1904 Rutherford's first great book *Radio-activity* appeared. He had become so famous that Yale University offered him $2,500 for a series of ten lectures—a fantastic fee for a scientist.

The United States sought to gain his full services: in the five years between 1903 and 1907 he was offered five different chairs —all of which he rejected.

In the following year a young German chemist arrived at McGill from Ramsay's laboratory to work under Rutherford. His name was Otto Hahn and no one dreamed that his name would later be associated with the most momentous discovery of all time—the splitting of the uranium nucleus—the foundation of the atomic bomb and the atomic machine. Rutherford was destined to die a year before the discovery was made and so was never to hear of it.

At McGill, however, Hahn was still an unknown man of twenty-six, full of enthusiasm and speaking poor English, for whom Rutherford at first had but little sympathy; but his important discovery that radio-thorium constitutes an intermediate stage between thorium and thorium-X—a fact which he had begun to suspect in London—won him the master's esteem. Even after Hahn had left Montreal for Berlin a close friendship united pupil and teacher, and they maintained a lively correspondence.

In spite of the pressure of work, Rutherford found time for extensive travels. Again he returned to New Zealand, travelling across North America and the Pacific. The following year he visited California again and lectured at Berkeley University— later the home of the cyclotron. In San Francisco the ashes of the great earthquake were still glowing; in wonder he gazed on them—a wonder akin to that produced later by the Grand Canyon of Arizona.

It now almost appeared as if Rutherford could enjoy a quieter life, after the hectic activity of the past years. He had bought a plot of land in Montreal and planned to build a house; then he was offered the Langworthy Chair of Physics in Manchester, an offer which he accepted. The house remained unbuilt. Briefly he bade farewell to the place, where for nine years he had worked at a superhuman rate—some fifty publications in nine years— and on 17th May 1907 the *Empress Of Ireland* slipped down the St. Lawrence with Ernest Rutherford aboard and set course for England.

★　　★　　★

When the widely travelled researcher returns to England to make it his permanent home, he is only thirty-six years old, and yet he is a famous man with three honorary doctorates, a Fellow of the Royal Society and of a number of scientific associations. The contrast between his age and his fame is so great that when he is presented to the Japanese ambassador, Baron Kikuchi, shortly after his return, the latter asks, 'Rutherford? Is that a son of the famous professor?'

In the unfriendly, sooty industrial town of Manchester Rutherford and his family occupy a handsome flat about a mile from the centre. His predecessor in the chair of physics, Arthur Schuster, famous for his work on optics, bequeaths to him a well-equipped department. And he bequeaths something else—his assistant, a twenty-five year old German physicist called Hans Geiger. Geiger, a man with an ingenious mind and great experimental ability, is to be of the greatest assistance to Rutherford during the five years they are to work together in Manchester. Later he is to devise an instrument well-known in our present atomic age as the Geiger counter.

Barely acclimatized to his new surroundings, Rutherford plunges again into his work. In the top storey of the Physics Building he stores his precious radium—at first only a few milligrammes, then later, thanks to the generosity of the Radium Institute in Vienna, more than 300 milligrammes. His most sensitive apparatus is located in a gloomy basement. Geiger later spoke of this room in the following way: 'One descended a further two steps and then heard Rutherford's warning to mind the heating-pipe, which was at eye-level, and the two water-pipes over which one had to climb. Then at last, one saw the great man sitting at his apparatus in the semi-gloom, and at once, in his incomparable way, he would tell of the progress of his experiments and of the difficulties he had just overcome.'

It was in this room that particles emitted by a radio-active substance were first counted. An alpha particle weighs only seven quadrillionths of a gramme—in figures 0·00000000000000000000007 gm.—but Geiger had devised apparatus—his first counter, later to be followed by other improved models—sensitive enough to register these incredibly small particles.

In Berlin at about the same time, another young German,

Erich Regener (later professor at the Technical High School in Stuttgart, where he became known for his research into cosmic rays at great heights and in considerable depths of water), was showing that an observation made eight years before by Crookes could also be applied to the counting of alpha particles. Crookes (and simultaneously Elster and Geitel in Brunswick) had found that luminous materials, exposed to alpha rays, were not uniformly luminous, but gave off countless minute flashes. Such a device he called a spinthoscope—and eyes accustomed to the dark can still detect the same phenomenon on the dial of a luminous watch. Regener suspected that every alpha particle produces a single flash. If so, it must be possible to count optically under a microscope these 'scintillations', and thus the alpha particles. And Regener did indeed find a value for the electrical charge of the alpha particles that corresponds closely to that assumed by Rutherford. Soon afterwards, Geiger, by comparing the electrical and visual methods of counting, confirmed the reliability of scintillation counting; this became for many years indispensable to research, and quite recently has gained much significance with the electrical—instead of the irksome visual—registration of flashes by a photo-cell as a 'scintillation counter'.

Amidst all the experimental activity in Manchester, where he had been for just a year, came in the autumn of 1908 the great news that Rutherford had been awarded the Nobel Prize! Ernest Rutherford is the eleventh physicist after Röntgen, Lorentz, Zeeman, Becquerel, Pierre and Marie Curie, Lord Rayleigh, Lenard, J. J. Thomson and Michelson to receive the highest honour that science can bestow. Yet what a surprise: Rutherford was awarded the Nobel Prize not for physics (which in 1908 went to the Frenchman Lippmann for his colour photography)—but for chemistry!

In his speech at the banquet in Stockholm the radiant young prizewinner related entertainingly how he had observed, in his research, many transformations—of thorium into thorium-X, thorium-X into thorium emanation, of this into radium-A, of radium-A into radium-B and many others. Yet none had been so rapid as his transformation from a physicist into a chemist!

In fairness to the Nobel Committee it should be added that

work on radio-activity lies in that indefinite borderland between physics and chemistry, and that even to-day it is not finally clear to which it belongs.

But while Rutherford was being honoured in Stockholm, his pupil Geiger had not been idle in Manchester. He had started the series of experiments on the scattering of alpha particles as they pass through metal foils; experiments that were to form the basis of a brilliant new idea of Rutherford's, of the second peak of his career, brighter perhaps than even the theory of radio-active decay: the discovery of the nucleus.

*   *   *

Many scientific advances hang for years barely perceptible in the air, gradually condense, and then the new idea is born, bringing new light and understanding, and indicating the future line of research. More than ten years earlier, the German physicist Philipp Lenard had been investigating electron rays in Heidelberg, Bonn, and Breslau (for which he won the Nobel Prize for Physics in 1905); he had been surprised that the electron rays, consisting as they do of tiny corpuscles, can penetrate metal foils with such comparative ease. As early as 1893 he had contrived to release into the air through one of these foils (the 'Lenard window') the rays produced in discharge tubes containing highly rarefied gas (to-day with a total vacuum).

How could the electrons fly through the atoms of the metals, which were assumed to be bound together so closely that the electrons could not, as it were, slip through between them? Lenard concluded that only small regions at the centre of the atoms are really impenetrable. These regions, which he conceived as strictly limited but powerful fields of force, he called 'dynamids'. But the time was not yet ripe for such a detailed conception to be followed up.

Now, a decade later, other scientists are even more surprised that the very much more massive alpha particles—complete helium atoms, 7,000 times heavier than an electron!—penetrate metal foils with such comparative ease. One man especially, who has been studying alpha particles intensively for ten years, is surprised: Rutherford.

He sets his students Geiger and Marsden to investigate systematically the penetration of metal foils by alpha particles, above all to measure their deflection and scattering. The first results are startling enough: most alpha particles are deflected only a very little. But a tiny fraction, clearly those which strike the 'impenetrable region' of an atom, fly off at a tangent to their original direction, or even back out of the metal like a ricochetting bullet.

This shows that the 'impenetrable regions' must be extremely small but also extremely massive, and a compelling idea takes shape in Rutherford's mind: every atom must possess a very small (even in relation to an atom's size) but very massive nucleus. And the deflection of the alpha particles must arise through a positive electric charge in the nucleus, by which— being positively charged themselves—they are repelled.

The final results of the experiments have not yet been reached, but the idea gives Rutherford no peace. He settles down to calculation, using formulae as he had previously used his measuring apparatus. And he arrives at an expression which states: making certain simple—the simplest possible—assumptions as to the nucleus of the atoms, the alpha particles *must* have this particular angular distribution. This formula, which first appeared in a letter of 9th February 1911 to the Leeds physicist W. H. Bragg, is still recognized to-day as 'Rutherford's Dispersion Formula'.

The experiments, whose final results Rutherford so eagerly awaits, are intensified. At last he snatches the paper with the results from Geiger's hand and stares at them: they show that the alpha particles are indeed distributed according to the formula he had worked out in advance! At this moment the nucleus is born; here is the beginning of a vast new development: now the nucleus, after millions of years of undetected existence and after being in the hands of the scientists—had they realized it—for fifteen years of research into radio-activity, suddenly emerges into the light of physical reality.

For the second time in his life, Rutherford's intuitive genius has sign-posted the path of progress. Only two years later a Dane, Niels Bohr, develops 'Rutherford's model atom', the nuclear atom, in which the electrons are arranged in some way as yet unknown around a small, massive nucleus, into the 'Bohr model atom' by gaining a more exact idea of the outer covering, of the arrangement of the electrons. A violent upsurge begins in nuclear physics. The spectra of the visible light rays are explained. Barkla finds the characteristic X-rays of the elements and Moseley measures their wave-lengths, after this has been made possible by Laue's discovery of X-ray diffraction by crystals. Hence the charge of the various nuclei can be measured and these prove to correspond with those very atomic numbers introduced by the chemists simply as ordinal numbers for characterizing the elements. One element ranges itself clearly beside another, one type of atom beside another, from hydrogen with the number 1 to uranium with the number 92.

This avalanche of scientific advances occurs in the few years 1911 to 1914; but in spite of all this wealth of discoveries and their interpretations, neither Rutherford nor anyone else can envisage the huge significance of the discovery of the nucleus; that there will spring from it the new science of nuclear physics, which in a few years will shake off all its fetters and break all bounds.

In the New Year Honours List of 1914 Rutherford was made a knight: he now became Sir Ernest Rutherford. There followed a series of journeys: in March he set out for Canada and the U.S.A. Back in England in May, he planned to go to Australia (where an important conference was to be held in Sydney) and to New Zealand. And in 1915 a big international congress of radiologists in Vienna was planned. It was to be inaugurated by Rutherford and Mme Curie, and scientists from all over the world were to discuss the amazing new developments.

But it happened otherwise. In Sarajevo on 28th June the shots were fired which shattered the veil which thinly covered violent political tensions. Yet, as there seemed to be no immediate danger, Rutherford started for Australia. At the beginning of August, however, all attempts to preserve peace failed; the First World War broke out. The curtain rose on a drama of blood and tears.

To-day after our experiences of a bloodier, more terrible conflict, we are astonished to realize how little normal civilian life was disturbed, especially at the beginning of the war. So we see Rutherford and many of his English colleagues, for all the clangour of war, peacefully discussing their problems in Sydney, half a world away from their home. And in spite of the German U-boats—whose activities are admittedly not yet at their height—they all return safely to England. Indeed, Rutherford first takes his wife and daughter to visit his parents in New Zealand, where he delivers a lecture in Christchurch at his old university, before returning in January 1915 after an uneventful trip (as he says in a letter) over the Pacific, across Canada and the Atlantic to Manchester.

The international fellowship of science, however, is disrupted —though occasional letters are exchanged between the physicists of the countries at war by way of a neutral state. Thus Rutherford writes to Geiger, who had gone to the Imperial Institute of Physical Technology in Berlin just before the war, taking with him Chadwick, who had the misfortune to spend the war in idle internment; and he writes to Stefan Meyer, director of the Vienna Radium Institute. But more and more the scientists are drawn into the war, either in the field (like the Germans Geiger and Hahn and the Englishman Moseley, whose promising career is cut off at twenty-seven by a Turkish bullet in the Dardanelles), or else in the laboratory doing important wartime research.

And so Rutherford is busy with war work, developing and improving sound locating equipment to meet the menace of the U-boats, which had soon become an acute danger to Britain, and might well have been mortal. Now all the resources of science are being organized and concentrated for defence. As leader of a group of British and French scientists, Rutherford goes to the United States, which have recently entered the war, to co-ordinate the research, development, and defence measures of the Allies. Gradually success rewards the united scientific and technological efforts of the Anglo-Saxon lands: U-boat losses rise; the tonnage of merchant shipping sunk decreases: the rate of new tonnage built begins to outstrip the sinkings—the same process as that repeated on a vaster, more perilous scale some twenty-five years later.

The First World War draws to its end. From the beginning the Central Powers have shed their blood in a vain struggle against odds too great for them; and now their strength fails. The victors dictate an injudicious peace, bearing in it the brand that was to set off a still more frightful conflagration.

The legacy of war is wretchedness, starvation, and chaos. Even for the victors the process of recovery is arduous and long. Slowly scientific research revives, though international contacts remain interrupted for a long time. Rutherford, who had now and then found time even during the war for the studies nearest his heart, devotes himself again to pure science. He is now nearly fifty, and his work has been held up for years by the war. Anyone would say that he has passed the peak of his career—two peaks, in fact, and both of tremendous importance to science— which is something seldom given to one man. He seems unlikely to achieve anything else of comparable importance.

But the unlikely happens! Before the end of 1919, at a time when the world is still groaning under the effects of war, when there is scarcely a laboratory that has fully resumed its activities, Rutherford is preparing his third and greatest stroke: he splits the nucleus!

Although Rutherford has long thought—and not infrequently suggested—that the immense force of the impact of an alpha particle striking a larger nucleus with a velocity of 15,000 or 20,000 km./sec. might well smash the latter, the actual discovery of a nucleus being thus smashed takes him by surprise, as a result of a minor observation incidental to some experiments with a quite different object. He is following up some earlier work of Marsden's, who had found that alpha particles passing through hydrogen thrust aside the hydrogen nuclei which are in their path with such violence that these latter themselves become radiation particles with great penetration; indeed, because of their small mass, they have an even greater range than the alpha particles which displace them. Rutherford now extends such experiments to oxygen and air. And here, too, he finds displaced oxygen and nitrogen nuclei (air being a mixture of the two gases), though of less penetration.

Most surprisingly, particles of extremely great penetration occur in air—but *not* in pure oxygen!—and these can only be hydrogen nuclei, H-particles. Yet there is no hydrogen present! Conversely, particles of even greater penetration are produced in pure nitrogen than in air. And now comes Rutherford's conclusion: the particles of extremely great penetration must be H-particles, hydrogen nuclei (which he later calls protons), that are knocked by the alpha particles out of the nitrogen nuclei— and *only* out of these, not out of those of oxygen. The nitrogen nucleus is split by the impact of an alpha particle!

In the midst of these exciting experiments, before the sensational results, which first appeared in the June (1919) number of the *Philosophical Magazine*, were known, burst a momentous letter from J. J. Thomson (now Sir J. J. Thomson), Rutherford's former teacher at the Cavendish Laboratory in Cambridge. Thomson is beginning to feel old; he wishes to resign his Chair, and to confine himself to his duties as Master of Trinity College. He asks Rutherford if he would care to take over the direction of the Cavendish, which is generally recognized as the leading Chair of Physics in England. And Rutherford says yes.

And so Sir Ernest Rutherford, on the threshold of his third great achievement, returns to Cambridge in the summer of 1919 as Cavendish Professor, returns as director of the Cavendish, whence he had set out twenty-one years before as a young man to conquer the world with his ideas.

★   ★   ★

Cavendish!—a name significant throughout the world, wherever physicists are at work. Maxwell, Lord Rayleigh, Sir J. J. Thomson have made the name famous, and now Sir Ernest Rutherford is to join the list of illustrious directors.

Here, too, there is no gradual acclimatization to the new circumstances. The splitting of the atom just discovered, but not yet positively established, urges Rutherford on. (Only later was it discovered that this was not really 'splitting' the atom, but the release of a proton from an atomic nucleus.) In the June number of the *Philosophical Magazine* appear the four basic articles. The first three merely substantiate the theory that under the impact of alpha particles on hydrogen, deeply penetrating particles are produced and that these are H-particles; further, they give the calculations of the speed of these particles and the proof of the production of nuclei of oxygen and nitrogen by the same process. The fourth article contains the sensation:

H-particles in pure nitrogen. Rutherford expresses himself very cautiously: 'In view of the results obtained, we can hardly avoid the conclusion that the particles produced by the collision of alpha particles and nitrogen nuclei are not nuclei of nitrogen but probably hydrogen nuclei or nuclei of mass 2. If this is the case, we must conclude that the nucleus of nitrogen is split by the tremendous force of the alpha particle with which it collides and that the nucleus of hydrogen produced thereby was previously part of the nitrogen nucleus.'

It is now a question of proving this more exactly and of establishing these surprising results, which at first met with doubt and opposition. This will provide work for the Cavendish Laboratory for the next few years.

A whole team of capable physicists is now working here: James Chadwick, twenty-nine years old and recently returned from German internment, the later discoverer of the neutron; C. D. Ellis, who collaborated with Rutherford and Chadwick in the production of the standard work on radio-activity, *The Radiation of Radio-active Substances*, which appeared in 1930; F. W. Aston, who discovered the isotopes of various elements with his mass spectrograph; twenty-three year old P. M. S. Blackett, who produced the conclusive photographs of alpha rays and nuclear transmutations in the Wilson cloud chamber; later come J. D. Cockcroft and the Irishman E. T. S. Walton, who were to succeed in producing nuclear transmutations with artificially accelerated protons; finally there is Peter Kapitza, a young Russian from Leningrad, who was fourteen years later detained in Russia, while on a visit there, and pressed into the service of that country.

Compared with his pupils, Rutherford does not now produce so many new results. Yet he remains the guiding spirit of the whole laboratory and it is more than probable that many of the results of his collaborators owe much to his ideas and inspiration.

The sensational release of protons from nitrogen nuclei by bombardment is extended to other elements. In 1924, all the lightest elements with the exception of lithium, carbon and oxygen have been split, by 1928 the number stands at thirteen. The word 'split' is, incidentally, a misnomer. Blackett's photographs prove that the alpha particle, which collides with a nucleus and releases a proton, remains in the nucleus and is incorporated into it. Since the alpha particle is four times heavier than the proton released, the bombarded nucleus is as a result heavier by three units of mass than before. We may speak of nuclear transmutation, therefore, but not of splitting the atom.

Disappointment dogs the steps of further developments; progress is terribly slow. It almost appears as if the atom is tenaciously defending its secrets against human intrusion. After thirteen years of intensive work by a whole team of researchers—in the Radium Institute in Vienna transmutation experiments are also in progress—the only result is that the nuclei of thirteen elements may all be transmuted in exactly the same way. Finally in 1932 there is a scientific land-slide and the sudden progress of nuclear research creates in a few years an entirely new situation.

In the meantime the fame of Sir Ernest Rutherford has brought him new burdens. At home and abroad he gives an incredible number of lectures to every sort of scientific society. For five years he is president of the Royal Society. Again he travels widely. In 1925-6 he revisits the Antipodes and sees his old parents again and lectures to excited audiences in his old university in Christchurch and in his home town, Nelson. In 1929, accompanied by his daughter, Eileen, and his son-in-law, the physicist R. H. Fowler, he visits South Africa, lectures in Cape Town, Johannesburg, and Pretoria, inspects the gold mines, the Natal National Park, the diamond mines at Kimberley, and the game reserve in Zululand.

The following year brings a bitter blow for Rutherford: his daughter dies on Christmas Eve, following the birth of her fourth child. Rutherford's intense love for his only daughter is now transferred to his grandchildren, and often he would linger at their bed-sides telling them good-night stories.

In the midst of his grief comes the culminating point in his public career. In the New Year Honours List for 1931 he is elevated to the peerage as Lord Rutherford of Nelson, New Zealand, and Cambridge. His arms include—in addition to a kiwi, that strange, long-beaked, New Zealand bird, and a Maori—the two crossed curves which symbolize the decay and replacement of radio-active substances—one of his earliest discoveries.

Shortly afterwards, great things begin to happen in the Cavendish. Cockcroft and Walton build high-tension apparatus in order to attack the nucleus from a new angle by bombarding it with protons which have been given the right amount of energy by means of high-tension electricity in a discharge tube. Chadwick builds on the discoveries of Frédéric Joliot and his wife, Irène, daughter of Mme Curie, and discovers the neutron. From America, too, which now begins to take a great interest in nuclear research, comes astounding news. And so begins the year 1932, a miracle year in the history of nuclear physics, which opens all locked doors and prepares the way for a series of new successes. Lord Rutherford sits in the Cavendish, in the centre of scientific activity, and can indulge, as few scientists have been able to do, in the Faustian feeling: 'This is my doing.'

*　　*　　*

Anyone who met Rutherford at this time, with his powerful figure, clear, cool eyes, energetic mouth, shadowed by a thick grey moustache, bare-headed, a great lock of hair falling over his face—more like an Australian farmer than a scholar in appearance—would never have thought that this man so positively alive, so full of bustling energy, should have but a few more years before him—years filled, however, with turbulent activity.

One scientific discovery follows on the heels of another: in the Cavendish Cockcroft and Walton transmute nuclei with artificially accelerated protons and Chadwick discovers the neutron. In Pasadena Anderson discovers the positron, in Berkeley Lawrence builds the cyclotron, and in New York Urey discovers heavy water. In Paris, shortly after this, the Joliot-Curies discover artificial radio-activity and open up new possibilities hitherto undreamed of.

Meanwhile the political firmament becomes ever gloomier: Hitler has come to power in Germany and the sound of the jack-booted brown-shirts marching through the Brandenburg Gate on 30th January 1933 echoes round the world. Slowly but surely

Germany is changed into a totalitarian state; slowly but surely German diplomacy becomes the instrument of uninhibited power-politics—which can lead to but one conclusion—war.

Those who do not of themselves recognize the danger which threatens, have their attention drawn to it by the flood of refugees which pours across the frontiers of the intolerant Reich—a flood of Jews and other 'non-Aryans', for the greater part members of the intelligentsia deprived of the very basis of their life in Hitler's Germany. Many of them are university lecturers; many of them are world famous. Einstein and Franck, Stern and Estermann go to the U.S.A., Hervesy goes to Denmark, Max Born and P. P. Ewald to Britain, and along with them go thousands more.

In England Rutherford helps with the work of absorbing the refugees. He is president of the newly founded Academic Assistance Committee. His warning voice is raised in protest against the suppression of scientific freedom and against intolerance and fanaticism. But sorrowfully he comes to realize that forces have been liberated which cannot be curbed by peaceful means and that everything is being swept irresistibly towards the catastrophe.

But Lord Rutherford was not to see the catastrophe. In the summer of 1937 his last book *New Alchemy* appears, in which he expounds the modern magic of the transmutation of elements. In the winter he hopes to attend a great conference in India. At the beginning of October he visits his country estate near Andover and appears to be enjoying perfect health. He returns home, feels unwell, and calls the doctor the following day. Then things move quickly. Strangulated hernia—operation—intestinal paralysis and blood-poisoning. On 19th October 1937, the fourth day of his illness, he dies.

* * *

With Ernest Rutherford's death a great epoch of scientific development which had lasted for forty years came to an end. From the first tentative penetration of the world of radio-active phenomena, the idea of the atomic nucleus has been evolved, started its victorious march and celebrated its triumphs. The mighty energies which this mysterious something contains have become visible and the artificial transmutation of elements has made real the dream of the alchemists.

But there was still one thing to do. All the nuclear experiments used tiny amounts of matter; their existence could be proved by their radiation, but the amounts of the new substances produced were small almost beyond measurement, and the energy liberated was correspondingly small. All thought of practical application waned in view of the tininess of the atoms, which had up to now been transmuted only singly or in small numbers in ingenious laboratory experiments. Even a genius like Rutherford saw no bridge between scientific experiment and technological application. The key which would unchain the atomic nucleus was not yet found.

More than once Rutherford, who had caused so many scientific miracles to take place, expressed his view as to the impossibility of producing atomic energy on a scale which would make it practically worth while. 'Probably we shall never be able to do so,' he said, 'and anyone who pursues such plans is on a wild goose chase.'

But in this Ernest Rutherford made a mistake. Even as he lay dying, his pupil, Otto Hahn, was already busy in Berlin with experiments which would within the year give mankind the key which was to liberate the gigantic energies of the Genie of the Atomic Nucleus.

2

RAYS RICH IN PROMISE

IT had been the mysterious rays, emitted apparently inexhaustibly and without recognizable cause by the element uranium,
which had caught and held the attention of young Rutherford
in 1898 and had finally led him to the discovery of the atomic
nucleus.

But even before this, before the concept 'atomic nucleus' had
in fact been born, both he and all other researchers working on
radio-active rays had in fact been working with atomic nuclei
without knowing it. In order to trace the origins of nuclear
research, we must therefore again go back in time to the middle
of the last decade of the nineteenth century.

What is an atomic nucleus, anyway? Before one can speak of
the nucleus of an atom, one must know something about the
atom itself! Should we, therefore, go back another hundred
years to the chemist Dalton, who founded the scientific concept
of the atom, or perhaps more than two thousand years to the
pre-Socratic Greek philosophers, Leucippus and Democritus,
who first conceived and expressed the idea of the atom?

Such an undertaking would not be an easy one, but fortunately
we do not need to embark on such a difficult task, since we are
here concerned with the history of the atomic nucleus rather than
the history of the atom itself. In order to understand the beginnings and course of this history, it is sufficient for us to realize
what was already known about the atom in the early nineties of
the last century. This is at the same time very much and very
little; little when one compares what was known then with what
is known now, but very much indeed when one considers how
much research, how much intuition and how much ingenuity

were required to collect the basic data about the atom in view of the often primitive nature of the apparatus available.

★   ★   ★

In 1890 an atom would be described as follows:

The atom is the smallest component, the smallest particle of a chemical element. An element, i.e. a substance which can no longer be broken down into other substances (e.g. hydrogen, oxygen, sulphur, iron, copper, gold, uranium), consists entirely of a number of tiny particles, each exactly the same as the others, and these are its atoms.

The atom is indivisible (in Greek a-tomos, hence the name).

There are as many sorts of atoms as there are elements. It is believed that there are ninety-two of these, although only seventy-five are actually known at the time. Elements can be ordered, tabulated according to their chemical behaviour (the famous 'Periodic System' worked out independently by the German, Lothar Meyer, and the Russian, D. I. Mendeliev, in 1869), but there are gaps in the table which must obviously correspond to elements still undiscovered. If we number the elements and the gaps in this table, hydrogen becomes number 1, oxygen 8, sulphur 16, iron 26, copper 29, gold 79, and uranium 92, so that each element, each sort of atom is characterized by a number— its 'atomic number'. (That the numbering was then slightly different, since some gaps had not been recognized as such, need not trouble us here.)

Atoms tend to collect together to form molecules. Similar atoms (usually two) produce a molecule of the respective element, dissimilar atoms (from two to a large number) a molecule of a chemical compound. Molecules consisting of dissimilar atoms are the smallest particles of a chemical compound and are always exactly the same for any given compound. Since water, for example, is a compound of oxygen and hydrogen, we have atoms of oxygen and atoms of hydrogen, but no atoms of water. There are, however, molecules of water, each one of which consists of two atoms of hydrogen and one atom of oxygen.

Every atom has a certain weight (to-day we say more correctly a certain mass). The relative weights of the individual types of atoms are well-known, even exactly known, from the chemical analysis of compounds. Thus it is known that the hydrogen atom is the lightest of all atoms; an atom of oxygen is 15·87 times as heavy, one of iron 55·40, and one of uranium 236 times as heavy. These relative numbers are called the atomic weights, at least after a slight adjustment: the chemists give oxygen the round number 16, so that the atomic weights are all increased a little—the atomic weight of hydrogen becomes 1·008, that of iron 55·85 and that of uranium 238. In the natural table of the elements the atomic weights increase constantly, if not evenly. The first element in the table, hydrogen, is the element with the lightest atoms, the last one, uranium, that with the heaviest ones. There are, however, a few mysterious and at that time completely inexplicable exceptions to this rule of the increasing atomic weight.

The real mass of the atoms (not only the relative numbers) is also known to a certain extent. Joseph Loschmidt in 1865 was the first to calculate the number of atoms in a gramme of hydrogen (or more precisely 1·008 grammes of hydrogen). He found a few 100,000 trillions. (To-day, the exact value of the 'Loschmidt number', which is accurate to within 0·1 per thousand, is 602,500 trillions, i.e. over half a quadrillion; this number of atoms would, if placed at intervals of one millimetre, reach two milliard times from the earth to the sun and back.) It follows from the number of atoms in one gramme that the mass of a single atom of hydrogen is roughly two quadrillionths (or more exactly 1·673 quadrillionths) of a gramme. With the aid of the relative numbers the mass of any given atom can thus be calculated.

The actual size of atoms is also more or less known: it is a few ten-millionths of a millimetre—several thousand times beneath the resolving power of the strongest microscope.

There is a final interesting observation in the description of the atom as it appeared in 1890: electricity, too, appears to consist of atoms, although of atoms of a different type. When an electric current passes through the solution of a salt or through acids, these compounds are broken down (by electrolysis) into their constituent atoms in such quantities as to suggest that the same amount of electricity was always associated with each atom separated; as if, in fact, a temporary combination of the particular substance and electricity had been formed—a combination of a material atom with an 'atom of electricity'. The electric charge of such an 'atom of electricity' may be measured: it, too, is terribly small—several trillions (more precisely 6·24 trillions) of these 'elementary charges' are necessary to produce a current of one ampère for one second. The atomic weight of these 'atoms of electricity'? Does electricity weigh anything at all? In those days this was still a completely open question.

In spite of the many individual detailed data, our description closes with a sceptical sentence: It is not known for certain whether atoms do actually exist. Many famous scientists regard the assumption of their existence as an uncertain hypothesis and deny their real existence.

*   *   *

Paris at the beginning of 1894. Amongst the two million inhabitants of this great city are three people, physicists, who, unbeknown to themselves, are destined to do great things. None of them is in contact with the others; none of them is at work on the atom. Within a few years, however, they will have made discoveries of an importance that will make their names known throughout the scientific world. These three people are: Henri-Antoine Becquerel, forty-one years old, of the Museum of Natural Science, Pierre Curie, six and a half years his junior and director of the scientific work at the municipal school of physics and chemistry, and Marya Sklodowska, a twenty-seven years old Polish student.

Professor Becquerel has already been at the Museum for two years. Even in appearance he is the typical French scholar with his high bald forehead and carefully trimmed beard. Not only is he personally a scholar, but he springs from a whole dynasty of scholars: both his father and grandfather had been professors in Paris and had worked at this same Museum of Natural Science on their chosen field of research—electrochemistry. His father studied the effects of light on electrochemical processes and obtained results which have since been known in the world of science as the 'Becquerel Effect'. Afterwards he devoted his attention more and more to fluorescent and phosphorescent phenomena, and his work in this field has been taken over by his son, who only two years ago had published the results of his own investigations in the *Journal de Physique*.

Pierre Curie, son of a Parisian doctor, still has no academic title but has been director of the scientific work at his school for the past eleven years, and in spite of unsatisfactory working conditions and wretchedly poor remuneration is still full of enthusiasm. Although, in collaboration with his brother Jacques, before embarking on his teaching career, he discovered the so-called piezo-electricity, the electrical charging of quartz crystals by expansion—a phenomenon which to-day plays a vital role in the production of high-frequency oscillations in the radio transmitter or in the ultra-sonic generator—although since coming to the school he has done important work on crystallography and on magnetism (Curie's basic law that the magnetic susceptibility depends on the temperature is a result of these investigations)—he has never bothered to try to improve his situation. An exaggeratedly modest man, honoured by his pupils as teacher and friend, he is torn between joy in his ever more absorbing work and the wretchedness of his material existence.

This is even more the case with the third and most interesting member of our trio, the student Marya Sklodowska. She is the daughter of a teacher of mathematics and physics at the Warsaw High School. The violent tension between the nationalistic Polish intelligentsia and the power of the Russian state had cast its shadow over her youth. She came to Paris two years ago, after a difficult time in Warsaw, where she earned her living by giving lessons and acting as governess in an uncultured family. Here, in Paris, she lives in the most penurious circumstances; hunger and cold are her daily companions. But this frail girl has untamable energy and courage: 'Our first principle should be not to let people or circumstances get us down', she writes on one occasion, or as she says in a later letter to her brother: 'You must believe yourself to have been born with a gift for some particular thing and you must achieve that thing no matter what the cost.'

And Marya Sklodowska believes in her gift. After her firs
year in Paris she passed her final examination in Physics and i
now about to sit for her finals in mathematics. The last yea
has not been an easy one. All her money was finished and i
seemed as if she must abandon her studies; then in the nick o
time she obtained through the good offices of a friend in Warsav
a scholarship which would enable her to continue her studies fo:
at least a further year, and by then she would have to reach he:
goal.

Now comes a meeting such as usually only happens in fair
tales.

At a social gathering in the spring of 1894 Marya Sklodowsk
is introduced to Pierre Curie. The impression on both sides i
deep and permanent; a conversation begins about scientifi
matters and gradually becomes more personal, a conversatio
which is never more to be interrupted. In the summer of the
following year they are married; Marya Sklodowska has become
Marie Curie, a name which will later assume almost mysti
proportions in the history of mankind and of science.

Meanwhile Pierre Curie has been granted the title of 'Pro
fessor' at his school, and the new dignity brings with it a sligh
improvement in his material circumstances, although they con
tinue to be extremely modest.

In this same year, 1895, Henri Becquerel becomes Professo
at the École Polytechnique.

In this same year, 1895, during the night of the 8-9th Novem
ber, the German scientist Wilhelm Conrad Röntgen sits in from
of his discharge tube in his laboratory in Würzburg in a state o
great excitement. The inductor which supplies the high
tension current buzzes. The glass walls of the tube shine with
green fluorescent light. The luminous screen lights up, and
when the scientist puts his hand between the tube and the
screen, it appears on the screen itself as a skeleton hand, as the
image of the invisible bone structure. A discovery of inestimable
significance has been made, a discovery that will provide the
impetus for an avalanche of new discoveries.

All the actors are now in position and our play can commence

★　　★　　★

Our drama opens on 20th January 1896, at a meeting of the Paris Academy. With the greatest excitement a crowd of scientists listens to the words of the well-known mathematician and physicist Henri Poincaré (a cousin of the lawyer Raymond Poincaré, president of the republic at the time of the outbreak of the war) who is speaking about Röntgen's discovery. He shows the first photographs which the German scientist has sent him: a frog, a human hand. Through the tissues the skeleton is shown clearly. Amazed, almost incredulous, these men of science look at the miracle. Poincaré describes how the mysterious rays responsible for the photographs are produced. By means of high-voltage discharge so-called cathode rays are produced in an electrical discharge-tube. Where these rays strike the inside of the walls of the tube, the glass fluoresces with a green light. From the fluorescent place new rays are emitted, which spread outside the tube, penetrate non-transparent objects and can be made to reproduce the skeleton image of a living object placed between them and a photographic plate wrapped in black paper.

Amongst the astounded and half incredulous audience there is one man particularly excited by Poincaré's words—Henri Becquerel. Fluorescence? Has he not been working with fluorescent or phosphorescent substances for years, with substances which when exposed to light, or even for a time after being exposed, give off light of a different colour? Might it not be possible that these mysterious rays are directly connected with fluorescence, that fluorescent or phosphorescent substances, exposed to sunlight, also send out such invisible rays, rays which have hitherto gone unnoticed?

The meeting is hardly over before Becquerel hurries to his laboratory and begins to experiment. He collects all his phosphorescent substances and manufactures a few more besides. In the course of the next few days he has a stroke of luck. The sun shines and Becquerel's substances all lie, neatly labelled, each on a photographic plate wrapped in black paper, in the sun for a few hours.

Now the exciting moment has arrived, which every scientist experiences when he is about to check the results of painstaking experiments; the moment which so often disappoints but which occasionally leads to an astounding new insight. Becquerel stands in the darkroom and develops his plates. And as so often —disappointment crushes his cherished expectations—there is not the slightest trace of an exposure on the plate. The next plate—nothing! The next—nothing! So the idea was wrong. Exposed, fluorescent substances do *not* emit penetrating rays. Yet, for the sake of order and completeness he develops all the other plates. And then—what is this? The seventh plate is definitely blackened! A quick glance at the list. What substance was exposed on the seventh plate? Number 5, 6, 7, there we are! Potassium uranium sulphate.

With renewed energy Becquerel plunges into weeks of experiment. Soon he has the answer: amongst the innumerable phosphorescent substances he has examined, a few do in fact emit invisible, penetrating rays when exposed to sunlight. They are, in addition to potassium uranium sulphate, sodium and ammonium uranium sulphate and uranium nitrate. Strange!— all these substances contain uranium—precisely this strange element right at the end of the table of elements.

In other respects, too, Becquerel has found out a few strange things. The visible luminosity of salts of uranium after exposure to the sun is very short, and barely lasts a hundredth of a second, but the invisible radiation is as strong as ever after a few days! Further, when an electroscope is placed near such a uranium compound it quickly loses its electrical charge. Obviously, the air, usually an excellent insulator, becomes slightly conducting owing to the invisible radiation—an effect which is incidentally known from Röntgen rays and is to be attributed to the formation of ions, of electrically charged molecules in the air. This 'ionization effect' was to be for the next few years the most important means of measuring radiation.

By the end of February Becquerel has made his first report to the Academy about the remarkable rays emitted by uranium compounds. Thereafter until the end of March a new report appears practically every week, for meantime Becquerel is on the tracks of a discovery of much greater dimensions.

The weather has broken. Day after day thick clouds obscure the sky.

In annoyance Becquerel has put his new uranium compounds

on top of his photographic plates in a drawer, since there is no
sunshine to which he can expose them.

A few days later the sun still refuses to shine, and the im-
patient scientist takes out his plates and develops them. They
have, after all, lain for a short time in dull light with the uranium
salts on top of them; perhaps there has been a slight blackening
of the plate in spite of the black wrapping paper. But the result
is quite different: the plates are as black, if not blacker, than
those which had lain in the sunshine with their uranium compounds! A thought flashes through Becquerel's mind: Could
*un*exposed uranium compounds . . . ?

Now follow feverish experiments.

Unexposed uranium compounds are placed on wrapped plates:
they blacken them. Samples of uranium nitrate are manu-
factured anew, completely in the dark: they blacken the plate.
Completely non-phosphorescent compounds of uranium are
tried, finally pure uranium: they blacken the plate.

In rapid succession the reports of Becquerel are published in
the *Comptes Rendues*—no less than seven appear in the course of
1896. In one of the latest he shows that a compound of uranium
newly prepared by him radiates as strongly after eight months as
it did in the first instance. And then for the first time he dares to
ask the question which goes to the root of these puzzling phenomena: From what source does uranium draw its energy in order
to radiate ceaselessly, inexhaustibly for weeks and months on
end?

In spite of the fact that Becquerel first called this radiation
'invisible fluorescence', he is quite sure that it is uranium which
is the bearer of all these phenomena, for all uranium compounds,
whether phosphorescent or not, emit the new rays in direct
proportion to their uranium content—pure uranium radiating
most strongly of all.

Gradually a new name for the rays is introduced. In France
and the neighbouring countries people begin to speak of 'Becquerel rays'—in Germany where the inseparable pair of researchers Julius Elster and Hans Geitel, teachers in the High
School at Wolfenbüttel, take up and confirm Becquerel's investigations; in Austria where the Viennese physicists Stefan
Meyer and Egon Ritter von Schweidler take up the work which

will lead to the foundation of the Vienna Radium Institute; and in England where J. J. Thomson and his research student Ernest Rutherford make their first experiments with the radiation of uranium.

But this name will not last either; two years later Mme Curie coins a name to cover the whole rapidly expanding field—'radioactivity', and this is a name which will stick.

*　　*　　*

Meanwhile the newly-married Pierre and Marie Curie, both obsessed by a mania for their work, have resumed their experiments, after spending their honeymoon cycling across the Ile de France. Marie has been permitted to work in the laboratory of Pierre's school. While her husband investigates the growth of crystals, she is experimenting on magnetism and at the same time gaining her final qualifications as a teacher. Conditions in the laboratory are very primitive: here and there the rain comes in, and the delicate instruments suffer from the damp. Their domestic conditions, too, are Spartan. The petroleum-lamp in their workroom sheds its weak light on a rough table, two chairs, and book-cases against the bare walls. Eight hours in the laboratory, three hours of housework, and then the study of scientific literature in the evening—this is Marie Curie's daily round. And after the birth in September 1897 of a daughter—who is named Irène, and who, like her mother, is already marked out for scientific fame—she has all the additional duties and cares of a mother.

But nothing can keep Marie Curie from her research work. She looks for a subject for a doctoral thesis, searching the most diverse fields of physics; for she cherishes the ambition of choosing a task which will lead her to break quite new ground. And her husband loyally assists her search for a fitting subject.

Finally her choice lights upon something that is still in its earliest stages: Becquerel's uranium radiation. Becquerel's first publications had appeared nearly two years previously, yet his discovery is still not widely known, and only some few other workers in other countries have tentatively begun to explore this new field. Practically nothing is known about the nature of the

Becquerel rays: here is the long-sought task that is worthy of a Marie Curie!

She needs a larger room for her work, and finds one in a cold, damp store-room on the ground floor of the school. In a few weeks the experiments are in full swing, and Marie Curie has soon confirmed Becquerel's results—that the most varied uranium compounds emit the mysterious rays. She extends her investigations to ever new substances, and shows that the intensity of radiation corresponds in every case *exactly* to the uranium content of the compound. Hence the radiation is a property of the uranium *atom*, and it is immaterial with what other atoms it is compounded. And again, the radiation shows itself to be completely independent of external conditions— of pressure or temperature—and of the state of the substance itself.

Always experimenting with fresh substances, Marie Curie discovers that not only the compounds of the metal uranium, but also those of the metal thorium, the element with the atomic number 90, emit similar rays, and that no other known element does. She was quite unaware that the same discovery was just being made by Gerhard Schmidt in Erlangen—a kind of duplication that often happens when a new scientific field is being opened up.

At last, when she has investigated every compound she can lay hands on, Marie Curie has an unusual idea: she tests the *minerals*, which she finds in the school's extensive collection of stones, among which are many containing uranium and thorium, for radio-activity. This, surely, is a mere waste of time—for will they not also emit radiation in proportion to their uranium or thorium content?

But this 'waste of time' brings a surprising result. Once more we are on the threshold of an entirely unforeseen discovery. Scarcely has Marie Curie investigated the first uranium-bearing minerals, pitchblende and chalcolite, when it is borne in upon her that the radiation is four times as strong as it should be, according to its uranium content. What is wrong? Not the analysis—the same result is repeatedly obtained: the radiation remains four times too strong!

And now one of those conclusions is being drawn, which arise unexpectedly from experimental results, but upon which far-reaching major hypotheses are built: hypotheses indirectly arrived at, but later confirmed by direct experiment. Marie Curie concludes that, as the mineral pitchblende emits radiation four times as strongly as it should, this can only be because it contains, apart from its known uranium content, a small amount of some other as yet unknown element, and that this is so radio-active that even a small admixture of it increases the radiation of the uranium mineral fourfold.

The sensational result is announced to the Academy on 12th April 1898 and is published in its transactions. Less than six months have passed since Marie Curie began her studies of radio-activity, and already a door is opening upon untrodden regions. Recognizing the great significance of the discovery, Pierre Curie gives up his investigation of crystals, and joins his wife in her researches into radio-activity, to which he will devote himself for eight years, until his tragic death.

Now they must redouble their efforts to solve this gigantic problem, of which Marie Curie had never dreamt when she was seeking a subject for her thesis: the problem of finding this unknown, mysterious element, whose presence in pitchblende, even in minute quantities, intensifies the radiation fourfold.

* * *

The analysis of pitchblende at this time is not very exact; it is a uranium ore, mined mainly in the Bohemian village of Joachimsthal and refined there, its salts being used for colouring glass. Its analysis is, however, sufficiently precise to allow at most a one per cent error for a suspected new element. It might just as well be only a thousandth. But then it must be several thousand times more radio-active than uranium. Hence it would be necessary to refine a few kilogrammes of pitchblende to obtain one gramme of the new element. Perhaps Pierre and Marie Curie would nevertheless lose heart, did they but know that the refinement not of a few kilogrammes, but of a few tons of pitchblende awaits them!

To seek by chemical means for a component of pitchblende which is present only in tiny quantities, and of which not even the chemical properties are known, would be almost hopeless. But the Curies have a miraculous guide who never deserts them: the mysterious radiation, whose intensification at once indicates in what part of the substance, which they are repeatedly breaking down chemically, the unknown element is hidden. Soon it becomes evident that there is a new, strongly radiant substance having the chemical properties of the metal bismuth in one of the reduced components. Marie Curie calls this polonium, in honour of her mother-country. Her report of it appears in July 1898.

Yet it immediately becomes clear that there is in all probability another strongly radiant element besides polonium present in pitchblende. They have been joined by a colleague in the school, G. Bémont, in the laborious reducing process, and now this element, with the chemical properties of the metal barium, is discovered in one of the reduced components. This newly-established element, clearly akin to barium, makes its appearance in the report of the session of the Academy of Sciences of 26th December 1898. The Curies call it *radium*. Thus, in a year's work, the substance is found which will soon have a meaning for the layman too; which, in thousands of clinics, will help man in his struggle against disease; which is the prototype of the whole group of radio-active substances.

But polonium and radium are still two unseen, intangible elements. Only their radiation betrays their presence in the reduced compounds of pitchblende. Their appearance, density, atomic weight, their physical and chemical properties are unknown. The only obvious fact is that they are present in pitchblende in extremely small quantities. The Curies must therefore refine a large amount of pitchblende to isolate a tiny amount of the new elements.

Moreover, a difference between them soon shows itself: when polonium is separated from uranium, its radiation decreases perceptibly in the course of a few months; that of radium does not. And so interest is concentrated on the latter. Yet there are still difficulties.

First the raw material. They need it by the ton. Eventually the Austrian government agrees to send a few tons of the then worthless pitchblende residue (the uranium, but not the radium, having been extracted), the Curies paying only the cost of transport.

Then the problem of finding somewhere to work. The bulky material requires something like a factory workshop. But there is nothing better than a wooden shed near Pierre's school: bare, wet, cold and draughty.

Finally the work itself. It is not the clean work with small quantities in test-tubes that scientists are accustomed to. No, they have to deal with hundredweights of material—more like workers in a cement factory than scientists tracking down a few milligrammes of a rare substance.

So it goes on for days, weeks, years. Pierre and Marie have divided the labour. Pierre checks the properties and radiation of the ever more concentrated radium preparations, while Marie attempts to refine them until they obtain a pure radium salt. Ever and again this grey mass of pitchblende—20 kilogrammes at a time—is saturated with acids, boiled, the solution is evaporated and fresh acids poured on. The shed is packed with large vats, so that there is scarcely room to move. When noxious gases are given off, the work must be done outside in the yard. In all weathers Marie Curie can be seen, moving the heavy containers or stirring the seething mass with an iron rod for hours on end.

At last the quantity becomes less. The ballast is discarded. The barium, which must contain the mysterious radium, is obtained as barium chloride. But the radium still has to be reduced to radium chloride. This can be done only by repeated fractional crystallization. The salt is dissolved in water, this is evaporated off, and the first parts to crystallize out become ever richer in radium.

Had progress not been clearly visible—from the stronger radiation of the new compounds—Marie and Pierre Curie might well have succumbed to the burden of their work, which becomes almost crushing when Marie, in financial difficulties because of the miserable remuneration of her husband, has to take a teaching post in a girls' school in Sèvres. Now she has her lessons to prepare and give, the household and the child—and the heavy work in the dreadful shed, where more and more glass dishes holding the extracts are piling up.

Yet the intensity of radiation in the samples keeps growing. A hundred, a thousand, ten thousand times that of uranium (always calculated on the basis of one gramme) has long since been passed. How long will it continue?

Finally, after nearly four years of superhuman effort, the goal is reached: Marie Curie holds a little glass vessel containing 1/10 gramme (100 milligrammes) of *pure* radium chloride. This is the yield from tons of pitchblende, the product of four years! But this pure radium chloride—a white salt, hardly distinguishable from cooking salt—radiates two million times more strongly than uranium!

Late one evening, when Pierre and Marie visit their shed in the dark, they are startled as they open the door. All the concentrated preparations are glowing in their glass dishes with a magical, bluish light, ghostly, unreal. The invisible rays, then, are now so intense that they actually cause a visible fluorescence —the opposite of what Becquerel had once assumed: that the fluorescence caused invisible rays. In the midst of this soft glow the Curies feel almost physically that the whole room is filled with mysterious rays. But they do not yet know that these rays are dangerous, that they can kill.

Marie Curie has the pure radium compound in her hands. Now she can determine the chemical properties of radium and measure its atomic weight. The chemical properties are very like those of barium, though the atomic weight is nearly twice as great: 225 (later, more exact value: 226·05). And so radium fits admirably into a gap in the table of elements, the gap with the number 88. The radium atom is now fully characterized, having its atomic number and atomic weight. The number of radio-active elements has risen to four: uranium, thorium, polonium, and radium. While the Curies have been working on radium, a fifth, actinium, has been discovered by their friend, the chemist André Debierne. It is element 89, that belongs in the gap between radium (88) and thorium (90). (The gap at 91 will not be filled until fifteen years later, by Otto Hahn with protactinium.) The German chemist Giesel succeeds in obtaining pure actinium; but it is unstable. Over a few decades it gradually disappears. And this applies with even greater force to polonium, which disappears in a few years. Only uranium, thorium and radium are stable; but the radiation of radium is millions of times stronger than that of the others—hence its unique significance.

Yet the coping-stone still remains to be set on this radium research: there are the pure radium compounds, radium chloride, and radium bromide (in which form alone radium later comes to be used, the form we mean when we speak simply of 'radium')—but the pure *metal* radium has not yet been obtained. Mme Curie, however, can add even this to her work, though not until eight years later, after the death of her husband. Producing metallic radium is a difficult process, and it has not been repeated since.

★   ★   ★

The Curies have long since made Becquerel's acquaintance through their work on radio-activity. They exchange ideas, especially about the dangers of radiation, after Becquerel suffered severe burning from a glass tube of radium carried in his waistcoat pocket, and after Pierre Curie has deliberately burnt himself with radium out of scientific curiosity. Marie Curie, too, has long borne irremovable traces on her fingers of the cruel element that she has disembedded from the grey mass of pitchblende.

A certain comradeship has developed between these three people, whose separate ways we have followed. Together they pursue their research into the little-known secrets of radio-active rays, and together they receive the highest recognition for their great discoveries: Henri Becquerel and the Curies together receive the Nobel Prize for Physics in December 1903.

To the Curies this honour means even more than it does to Becquerel. For one thing, the considerable sum of money attaching to the award—they get some 70,000 frs.—relieves the straitened circumstances, which, incredible though it sounds, have up to now over-taxed the energies of these famous scientists. Now Pierre Curie can give up his post at the École de Physique and devote himself to research. But Marie—untiring in her passion for work—still travels to Sèvres several times a week to teach the girls there.

The major significance of the Nobel Prize for the Curies, however, lies in the wide international recognition it brings—

such as France has not yet accorded them. A year previously Pierre Curie, who helped to discover radium, has been passed over in the elections to the Paris Academy of Sciences in favour of a much less important candidate; neither has he, let alone Marie, a university Chair. The only laboratory they have is still the few cheerless, make-shift rooms in the school.

Weighed down thus with their work, Pierre and Marie Curie are so exhausted that they cannot find the strength to make the winter journey to Stockholm to receive the prize from the hands of the King of Sweden. They ask to postpone making their speeches in Stockholm. And so Marie Curie misses the celebration of her triumph, only six months after taking her doctorate, of being the first woman to gain the Nobel Prize, the highest scientific honour. The second Nobel Prize for science to be awarded to a woman was to fall to this same Marie Curie eight years later; and the third—and up to now the last—to her daughter Irène: a list of achievements that is, and may well remain, unique.

The researches of the Curies proceed laboriously, no longer overcast by material cares, but now by the struggle for reasonable working conditions. They are worn out by the search for a proper laboratory and by their work in the incredibly primitive shed. Matters are not improved by Marie's second pregnancy, until, despondent and incapable of any activity, she gives birth to her second daughter, Eve-Denise, in December 1904—just a year after receiving the Nobel Prize. It is Eve-Denise who, decades later, is to write the moving and inspiring biography of her famous mother.

As her interest in the baby grows, Marie Curie's resilient nature triumphs over the depression to which many women might have succumbed. Circumstances slowly change for the better: at last Pierre has obtained the coveted Chair at the Sorbonne, and with it a deputy, an assistant, and a laboratory assistant—but still no laboratory! Marie becomes Pierre's deputy, and so is employed by the university at a salary of 2,400 frs. (by no means a lot for the Nobel prizewinner who had discovered radium!)—yet she still continues her teaching in Sèvres. After a further year, Pierre finally enters the Academy of Sciences.

The struggle for a laboratory goes on: Pierre has at least contrived to get two rooms built on the Rue Cuvier as a start, though this is insufficient, as young physicists and chemists from all over the world are flocking to the Curies, to learn from them the new science of radio-activity. The one advantage is that the Curies can now give up their shed and transfer their apparatus to the Rue Cuvier. Pierre Curie, however, carries on the struggle: he wants—and needs—an Institute with numerous rooms in which to pursue his own research and also to instruct a sufficient number of young people to continue the work after him.

Where the granting of money is concerned, the state can be unimaginably tight-fisted. Hopes are raised only to be dashed again.

Then, in the midst of these hopes and disappointments, fate strikes: on the dull, wet afternoon of 16th April 1906, at the junction of the Pont Neuf and the Rue Dauphine, Pierre Curie falls beneath the hoofs of the horses and the wheels of a heavy dray. His skull is crushed. Death is instantaneous.

Events repeat themselves. Pierre Curie, not yet forty-seven, has been snatched with startling unexpectedness from his work. At this time Henri Becquerel is fifty-three, in robust health, a keen swimmer and mountaineer. Two years later he becomes President of the Academy in Paris, and also its permanent Secretary. Is this of evil omen? In this year 1908 he is the third person to fill this post. Two have died within a short time before him.

In the summer he goes to the seaside, full of youthful vigour. No one can believe the news that spreads a few days later: Henri Becquerel has died after a heart-attack at Le Croisic in Brittany on 25th August.

*　　　*　　　*

Of the three people we have followed in their quest, which brought to light the new science of radio-activity, there remains but one: Marie Curie. The sudden and terrible death of her husband has left her apathetic, indifferent to the claims of life. These are re-asserted first by her scientific work. Years before, Pierre Curie had once said: 'Whatever happens, even if we should be left a soulless body, we must go on working in spite of everything!' And this becomes Marie's guiding principle. And perhaps it is the best thing for her that a mass of work is awaiting her.

The Sorbonne—not without much heart-searching over the decision, unheard-of in 1906, to appoint a woman to the teaching staff of the university—offers her the succession to her husband as director of the laboratory and to his Chair (in 1908 she is given the title of Professor). She summons all her strength, accepts, and on 5th November of the ill-starred year 1906 she stands for the first time at the front of a crowded lecture-room. Thus, for women the world over, Mme Curie has breached the wall of prejudice and conservatism—whose razing took several more decades. Five years later, only six months before receiving her second Nobel Prize, Marie Curie is rejected by the Paris Academy of Sciences because 'a woman cannot become a member'!

Mme Curie is again in control of herself, though she never really recovered from the blow that had befallen her. Her face has grown hard; her eyes have lost their fire of enthusiasm; her hair has greyed. For twenty-eight long years she sees with a certain aloofness the successes that radium brings, she attains world fame (which troubles her, and which she seeks to evade), she sees a new branch of science blossom from the seed she had sown.

What Pierre Curie had dreamed of in vain is now fulfilled: the building of a large Institute, to be devoted to research on radium and radio-activity. External circumstances come to Mme Curie's aid: the value of radium in medicine has been discovered. 'Curie therapy' is developing. The radium industry grows up first in France, and the mysterious substance that existed only in laboratories for its scientific interest now acquires a market value which is more than a hundred thousand times that of gold. The gramme of radium which Mme Curie's labours had extracted from valueless material is suddenly worth a million francs. But the Curies had never thought of amassing a fortune; when Pierre was still alive they had rejected the idea of patenting their process. And so now Mme Curie presents her gramme to the laboratory, and does the same with another gramme sent her as a gift from the American people.

And so the Institute is being built. The road where it will stand bears the name Rue Pierre Curie. Meanwhile Mme Curie and André Debierne have succeeded in producing pure metallic radium, and in December 1911 she is awarded the Nobel Prize for Chemistry. She goes to Stockholm, accompanied by her fourteen-year-old daughter Irène, who, twenty-four years later, will participate in the celebrations as the guest of honour. The money she wins is invested in war loan, and a few years later has been rendered valueless through depreciation.

In July 1914 the Institute is finished. But before it can open, the war breaks out. Once again Mme Curie finds much to do: she sets up mobile X-ray vans and permanent X-ray stations—of which the French army, in spite of nineteen years of X-ray development, has virtually none—thus saving the lives of thousands of wounded. When the Germans overrun the Marne in September and threaten Paris, Mme Curie takes her gramme of radium to safety in Bordeaux (in a lead-lined crate weighing over 40 lb., on the overcrowded refugee trains!); but she herself returns to her chosen tasks in Paris.

After the war the Radium Institute is inaugurated. It has two departments, one for pure research into radio-activity under Mme Curie's direction, the other for biological investigation and the development of the 'Curie therapy'—the medical application of radio-active rays—which is in the charge of a well-known doctor, Professor Claude Regaud.

Students from all countries flock to this fountain-head of the new science; among them there later appears a highly gifted Frenchman, Frédéric Joliot. He becomes friendly with Mme Curie's daughter Irène, who has also just completed her course in physics. The romance of 1894 repeats itself: their marriage in 1926 establishes a research team that is destined to continue and complete the work begun by Irène's parents.

During these busy years, Mme Curie sees the grandiose development between the wars of the branch of science that is so much her own; she is able to follow the meteoric rise of Rutherford and the discovery of the nucleus, which leads to the exact localization of the processes within the atom, something that had always been her own field of study. And now she lives to see the fascinating sequel to her work—the first splitting of the atom, the artificial transmutations of the nucleus. She sees the crowding new discoveries of this year of miracles 1932, and just lives to see the session of the Paris Academy of January 1934, when her daughter Irène and her son-in-law report on the discovery of artificial radio-activity—the crowning of Marie Curie's own efforts.

When the first shadows lie menacingly over Europe after Hitler's dramatic seizure of power, Mme Curie's life has run its course. Symptoms of an inexplicable disease show themselves. She declines rapidly, and the doctors can do nothing for her. On 4th July 1934, at the age of sixty-seven, Marie Curie dies in a sanatorium in the French Alps.

The medical diagnosis says: pernicious anaemia, yet the symptoms and the blood-tests deviate from the normal pattern. The marrow of the bones has ceased to react, as it has been permanently damaged by decades of exposure to radiation.

The radium, which she released like a phoenix from the dross, has carried Marie Curie to the highest peak of fame.

Now radium has killed her.

3

SLEEPLESS NIGHTS OVER
A FEW DEGREES RISE IN TEMPERATURE

IN order to trace fully the life of an inspired researcher we have jumped forward in time and touched on events and people which belong to a later period of historical development. We must now turn back to the years immediately following the discovery of radium, years abounding in new discoveries, which only gradually begin to form a clear picture. We must now examine the research into that quality which distinguishes in such a marked fashion radium and other radio-active elements from normal substances—we must examine the research into radio-active radiation.

Radiation was already known in the world of physics at this time. Recently Röntgen had discovered his penetrating rays with their remarkable properties which had already begun their triumphal march in the sphere of medicine. The exact nature of these rays was not known: many scientists believed that they moved in waves like light, but in that case they should be slightly bent when passed through a narrow slit, and should fan out to cover a certain angle, as does actually happen in the case of light. Yet the scientists could find no evidence of this.

Many scientists therefore doubted whether Röntgen rays did move in waves, but believed them to be corpuscular rays, made up of minute particles travelling at high speed. The most important man to hold this opinion was W. H. Bragg in Adelaide in distant Australia, a man who is later to receive along with his son the Nobel Prize for work on X-rays. But in his explanation of X-rays as corpuscular rays W. H. Bragg was wrong. For a long time the dispute continued, until in 1912 Max von Laue showed *how* one should look for this bending of the rays. Then at last they were proved to be bendable, and the dispute was settled: X-rays are wave rays but the length of the waves is 1,000 to 10,000 times shorter than the wave-length of light (which is itself only a few ten-thousandths of a millimetre).

There were, however, other rays which were manifestly corpuscular rays—cathode rays, which are produced in a glass tube with an extremely rarefied gas content, when the two metal openings in the tube (the cathode and the anode) are connected to a source of high voltage. These are rays which, on striking some obstacle, produce in the tube the completely different X-rays. Cathode rays are produced by the negative electrode, the cathode, and travel in straight lines. This was discovered as early as 1858 by Julius Plücker in Bonn; it was almost twenty years later, however, that the term 'cathode rays' was first used by Eugen Goldstein. Another ten years after this, in 1886, this same Goldstein had discovered a second type of ray in an electric charge. On account of the special nature of their production he called them canal rays, and they travel through the discharge tube in the opposite direction to the cathode rays, not from the anode but from the space containing gas (on first being produced through holes—'canals'—in the cathode). The two types of ray, travelling in opposite directions, clearly consist of particles containing opposite charges, those of the canal rays having a positive, those of the cathode rays having a negative charge.

Towards the end of the nineteenth century many researchers had started work on the rays produced in an electrical discharge tube. The cathode rays established the fame of the German physicist Philipp Lenard, who succeeded in releasing the rays from the tube by means of a 'window' of extremely thin aluminium foil which they can penetrate. In 1905 he received the Nobel Prize for physics for his ingenious and thorough researches into cathode rays.

But now, at the end of the nineteenth century, the question as to the exact nature of the particles, which, travelling at what must be a very high speed, constitute the cathode and canal rays, was one which became acute. Are they electrically charged molecules or atoms? Or are they those mysterious and as yet intangible atoms of electricity, whose existence had, as we have seen, been indicated by the electrolytic decomposition of solutions of salts and acids—those mysterious atoms of electricity for which, in spite of their hypothetical nature, the name 'electrons' had gained currency?

A means of answering this question appeared when it was discovered that both cathode and canal rays could be deflected by a magnetic field, and also by the electrical field of force between two charged plates—deflected according to the nature of the charge of the particles, the two types of ray being deflected in opposite directions. From the sum of the two types of deflection (magnetic and electric) it should be possible to calculate not only the speed (the faster the particles travel, the more difficult it becomes to deflect them) but also the ratio of the charge of a particle to its mass. What will the result of this calculation be? Will it be the charge/mass ratio already known from electrolysis, which would point to charged atoms?

In the year 1897 a whole crowd of researchers into cathode rays arrived at a solution of the problem. Surprisingly enough the charge/mass ratio is not the same as for electrolysis, but a few thousand times greater. Since they always worked with the same charge, only one conclusion could be drawn: the negatively charged particles travelling in the cathode rays are a few thousand times lighter than the atoms. Clearly they are the long-sought-after atoms of electricity completely liberated from matter, they are free electrons! These electrons, then, do have a certain weight, even if a very slight one. Electricity weighs something too! Exact measurements show later that the mass of an electron (to-day we say more correctly the 'rest mass' since the mass becomes greater when moving quickly) is 1,837 times smaller than the mass of the lightest atom—the hydrogen atom.

Still there was no trace of positive atoms of electricity. In the very next year Willi Wien, a German physicist in Aachen, succeeded in making the corresponding measurements for the canal rays. And now there was a new surprise. It is not positive electrons which make up the canal rays, but rather positively charged atoms and molecules (according to the nature of the gas in which the discharge takes place), that is to say ions.

The search for the positive electrons continued, but in vain. The electron appeared only to exist as a negative particle, while there were both negative and positive ions. Another thirty-four years have to pass before the positive electron is discovered as a rare phenomenon which only occurs under certain very special circumstances.

The speed of the particles constituting canal and cathode rays is extremely high and increases in direct proportion to the voltage used in the production of the rays. At 10,000 volts the electrons in the cathode rays travel at 36,000 miles per second, at 100,000 volts at 103,000 miles per second—at half the speed of light (186,000 miles per second in a vacuum). The heavier particles in the canal rays, the ions, travel several hundred times more slowly than the free electrons in the cathode rays, but even so travel many hundred miles in a second, exceeding the speed of a modern jet fighter by several thousand times.

Thus three different types of ray were known at the turn of the century in addition to the Becquerel rays:

Cathode rays—rays made up of negative electrons, travelling at speeds from 30,000 to 90,000 miles per second when produced by normal high voltages; *Canal rays*—rays made up of various types of positive ions, travelling at speeds from 120 to 600 miles per second when produced by normal high voltages; *X-rays*—rays moving in waves like light (still unproved) and travelling at the speed of light—186,000 miles per second.

Canal rays can be deflected to one side, cathode rays to the opposite side by means of electric and magnetic fields, X-rays cannot be deflected.

Canal rays are held back by the thinnest metal foil, cathode rays penetrate thin sheets of metal foil, X-rays can penetrate thick layers of metal.

These few sentences form the basis from which we must examine the newly-discovered Becquerel rays, the rays produced by radio-active substances.

★   ★   ★

The discovery of radio-active rays occurred in the last years of the period of discoveries associated with the gas discharge rays, which they resemble in many respects. When Henri Becquerel made his surprising discovery, the free electron was not yet known, nor was anything definite known about the nature of the particles constituting the cathode and canal rays. But this knowledge was gained in the next few years, in those very years when our picture of the Becquerel rays and the nature of radioactive substances began to take shape.

Naturally, that picture was, to begin with, a very confused one. One observation supports another, only to be contradicted by a third one. Often it is difficult to say who first made a certain discovery. In 1900, for example, the Frenchman Villard observed a penetrating type of ray (later called gamma rays); in the same year Becquerel observed them, too, and a little later Rutherford. In 1903 Rutherford was the first man to discover the magnetic deflection of alpha rays, but in the same year so did Becquerel and the German physicist Des Coudres. Everywhere radiological research institutes were being built. The Curies, Becquerel, and Debierne were at work in Paris, then Rutherford and Soddy in Montreal, Dorn (the first to discover radium emanation) in Halle, Giesel in Brunswick, Elster and Geitel in Wolfenbüttel, Schmidt in Erlangen, Meyer and Schweidler in Vienna, and many more elsewhere.

What were the media through which these scientists made their observations? In the first years there were really only three:

First, the photographic plate, which becomes blackened when exposed to radio-active radiation.

Secondly, the fluorescent screen (which played such an important role in Röntgen's discovery), a sheet of cardboard covered with a radio-active material which lights up when sufficiently strong radio-active radiation strikes it.

Thirdly, the ionization of the air through radio-active radiation; that is to say, the air becomes slightly conducting under the influence of the radiation, so that electrically charged bodies which have been isolated gradually lose their charge. The widespread leaves of a gold-leaf electroscope, for instance, gradually close up when the electroscope is exposed to radio-active radiation. The more quickly they close up, the stronger the radiation. This is thus an easy way of measuring *quantitatively* the strength of the radiation, which is the first step, which must of necessity be made as soon as a new branch of science has passed beyond the mere qualitative descriptive stage, when it is a question of discovering laws.

Then arises the question: Is it possible to change radio-active radiation by means of external interference? The scientist is never satisfied with what nature offers to him; he extracts the confession of her secrets with the most forceful means; all the achievements of the exact sciences have had to be wrung mercilessly from a recalcitrant and unwilling nature.

How, then, can radio-active rays be changed by interference from without?

One thing was soon discovered: a change in the condition of the radio-active substance does not have any effect on the radiation. A radio-active substance may be melted, or chemically compounded with other substances, it may be exposed to extreme heat or cold or subjected to the strongest electrical and magnetic forces, and yet the total strength of its radiation remains completely unchanged. Occasional observations to the contrary, for example when a radio-active preparation, on being heated, did not radiate so strongly, were proved to be incorrect, in so far as it was shown that a part of the radio-active substance had been lost in the process of heating—a radio-active gas, or an emanation, which had previously been imprisoned in the substance, had been liberated and so taken part of the 'activity' with it. This part of the activity had not disappeared, but merely changed its location and appeared again in the place where the gas settled. The complete independence of the radiation from the external condition of the radiating material is significant in that it shows that the radiation springs from the inner depths of the radio-active atom, from depths to which neither thermal, magnetic, electrical nor chemical forces can reach.

Once the rays have left the radiating material, however, there are various possibilities of changing them.

They can be passed through other substances, through thinner or thicker layers of this or that material. Even the air is such a 'material'. In a vacuum the strength of the rays is different from what it is when they have passed a certain distance through the air. It proves that all substances have a certain weakening effect on the rays passed through them. This 'absorption' of radio-active radiation in matter became one of the most important means of investigation.

It was shown by means of the principle of absorption that the radio-active radiation of most of the preparations used at the time represented a mixture of various types of ray. Some were absorbed completely by very thin layers of solid material, others appeared to be absorbed only by thicker layers. As early as 1898 Rutherford distinguished the readily absorbed 'alpha' rays from 'beta' rays, which are not so easily absorbed. When Villard discovered a third, very penetrating type in 1900, they were called 'gamma' rays.

The varying range of penetration of these rays appears even in the air around us, where under normal conditions alpha rays will travel only a few inches, while beta rays travel a few yards and gamma rays a very great distance before being absorbed.

The ionization effect of the three types of ray is inversely proportionate to their penetrating power. In 1902 Rutherford established that the ionization effects of alpha, beta and gamma rays stand in the relationship of 10,000 : 100 : 1. But why should this be inversely proportionate to the penetrating power? The less a ray ionizes in the course of its passage through matter, the less energy it expends in dividing atoms into charged particles, and the further it can travel before becoming exhausted.

We have still to mention the most important means of interfering with the course of radio-active rays. By means of a spherical lead container with a very narrow opening it is possible to select one 'pencil', one ray, as it were, out of the rays radiating in all directions. Electrical and magnetic forces can then be brought to bear on this single ray, which usually travels in a perfectly straight line. Would it be possible to deflect this ray?

*　　*　　*

As in the case of the cathode and canal rays, electric and magnetic deflection fulfilled the hopes placed in them. Not immediately, however, for the explanation of the nature of the various rays had to wait five years and some important pieces of information were only gathered very much later still.

Here too, the course of events was somewhat confused. The magnetic deflection of beta rays was one of the first results. Last of all it proved possible to deflect alpha rays by means of electric and magnetic forces; for a long time they were held to be incapable of deflection, since a deflection is only to be observed when the rays are exposed to very strong fields of force. Even the strongest forces proved unable to deflect gamma rays, which resemble X-rays in this respect; indeed, it became increasingly clear that the two types of ray are closely related.

The final result of the most varied investigations may be summarized as follows:

Alpha rays = rays of positive ions (like canal rays); these are helium ions (to-day we should say helium nuclei) carrying a double positive charge. Speed: 9,000 to 13,000 miles per second.

Beta rays = rays of (negative) electrons like cathode rays, their particles being exactly the same as those of the cathode rays. Speed: 125,000 to 186,000 miles per second.

Gamma rays = waves (like X-rays except that their wavelength is shorter than that of any X-rays which could then be produced). Speed: speed of light (186,000 miles per second).

Some of this information was only gained later, e.g. the exact measurement of the speed of the electrons in the beta rays. Only very recently (1951) was it possible to measure the speed of gamma rays directly.

Alpha and beta rays are corpuscular rays. When compared with canal and cathode rays they prove to move at a much greater speed. The corpuscles which make up the former rays therefore must have greater kinetic energy than those of the latter. It is not difficult to calculate the voltage (assuming single charges) to which the particles of the canal rays or the electrons must be subjected in order to reach the energy-level of the alpha or beta particles. It was discovered that the alpha particles correspond to a potential of 4 to 9 million volts and electrons of the beta rays to a potential of 1 to 4 million volts (in spite of their higher speed their kinetic energy is lower, since they are lighter!). Later it became customary to express the energy of such high-speed atomic particles in voltages. This unit of energy is called 'electron-volt', thus we say that an alpha particle has a kinetic energy of 4-9 million e.v. (electron-volts) or 4-9 M.e.v. At this time and for years to come alpha particles of radio-active radiation were the most powerful atomic particles known. Their energy is a hundred times greater than that of the most powerful canal rays which could then be produced. It was therefore

natural that they should be used two decades later as the firs
atomic 'missiles' in the attempts to 'split' the atom.

There is another striking thing about the electrons of the bet
rays. In some radio-active substances their speed is almost tha
of light (up to 99%) but never in fact reaches it.

In these years of early research into radio-activity, in 1905 t
be precise, an almost unknown physicist, a minor official in th
Swiss patent office in Bern, propounded the following concis
theorem: 'No physical body can exceed the speed of light o
ever reach it completely.' The young physicist was called Alber
Einstein. The theorem is part of an extensive theory, to-da
famous throughout the world—the Theory of Relativity. Thu
we begin to see why the Theory of Relativity will later play ai
important role in the physics of atomic particles.

In 1903, however, nothing was known of this. In other respect
also the characterization and classification of the types of radio
active radiation were not so complete and clear as we hav
suggested here. However, by the end of 1903 the most importan
work in the differentiation of the three types of radiation and thei
properties had been completed. The barriers which protect th
secrets of radio-active matter had been broken down and the wa
seemed open for rapid progress, when a new obstacle arose.

*   *   *

It was Pierre Curie who raised this new problem in the spring o
1903. Both he and other scientists had been pondering over th
origin of the inexhaustible radiation emitted by radium, uranium
and thorium. Day and night, unceasingly and in constan
strength, these substances emit rays. What is the source of th
energy which manifests itself in the high-speed ray-particles?

'From nothing comes nothing!', had been the cry raised som
sixty years previously by Robert Mayer, a doctor in Heilbronn
a man long unrecognized and rejected by many as a madma
when he had maintained that there was such a thing as energ
which could appear in the most varied forms, as movement, a
heat, as light, as electrical energy, and which could change fron
one form to another, but which could under no circumstance
arise from nothing or disappear into nothing.

Robert Mayer was long dead and the times when his theory was rejected were long past. We are now in the enlightened age of energetics. Energy is the idol of the physicists and the theory of energy is an unquestioned axiom. Now, however, a few strange substances are discovered which do not seem to take notice of this axiom, but which radiate and radiate as though there were no such thing as the theory of energy.

Do these substances prove the theory of energy to be wrong? Must the theory now be rejected? Is energy here really arising from nothing? Or does the energy spring from some mysterious source of original energy on which the radio-active atoms are able to draw?

Pierre Curie did not indulge in wild speculation; he decided to measure the energy continually emitted by radium. The energy is emitted from the radio-active preparation in the form of rays, but the greater part of these rays are not very penetrating and do not get further than the preparation itself or the walls of the container. There the energy must be changed into heat and it should be possible to prove the presence of this heat!

Pierre Curie and his assistant, Laborde, set to work. Two grammes of barium chloride were placed in two similar glass tubes. But only one of the preparations was pure barium chloride—the other contained a sixth part of radium chloride. Both tubes were placed under the same conditions in a room with a constant temperature, protected against draughts, each tube being provided with a thermoelement—a very sensitive electric thermometer.

The immediate result was that the tube with the radium showed a temperature one and a half degrees higher than that of the other tube.

One and a half degrees is not much. Perhaps the thermometer was wrong? A check on two tubes both containing pure barium chloride showed a difference of 0·01 degrees.

The experiments were varied. A more concentrated preparation of radium produced an increase in temperature of three degrees. The result is irrefutable: radium produces heat constantly and this heat is an indication of the energy constantly being liberated.

When Pierre Curie reported on the results of his experiments to the Paris Academy, he had already discovered still more. He had discovered how much electrically produced heat—which can be measured exactly—has to be used to bring the tube with the pure barium chloride up to the same temperature as the tube 'heated' by radium. In this way he had measured the heat produced by the radium and could express it in calories—one gramme of radium gives off in one hour some 100 gramme-calories of heat.

★   ★   ★

Neither one and a half degrees nor 100 gramme-calories represent very much. 100 gramme-calories would just be sufficient (if no heat were lost) to increase the temperature of 100 grammes of water—about a wine-glass full—by one degree.

But these ridiculous few degrees rise in temperature create a sensation in the scientific world. 100 gramme-calories in an hour mean 2,400 gramme-calories in a day or 2·4 kilocalories, 8 kilocalories in three days—the same amount of heat as is obtained from one gramme of coal, 1,000 kilocalories in a year, in a thousand years a million kilocalories, in . . .

Enough! This is fantastic! Can we reckon in thousands of years? Who can say whether a gramme of radium is still radiating as strongly after a thousand years, or even whether it is still radiating at all? Pure compounds of radium have been known for exactly one year, but in this period and in the seven years that the radiation of uranium and thorium has been studied no diminution of their radiation has been observed. But does this prove that these substances are eternally inexhaustible?

The fact that the radiation of a whole series of radio-active substances does manifestly become weaker, and that these substances can be exhausted must give the researcher pause. The radiation of polonium, for example, is only half as strong after four and a half months, that of thorium-X diminishes by a half within three and a half days, while that of thorium emanation lasts only for one minute.

Only uranium, thorium and radium are constant. But are they constant for thousands of years, for all eternity? Rutherford and Soddy have just published their Theory of Radio-active Decay, and if their theory is true, it means that all radio-active atoms change, including the atoms of radium, thorium and uranium; these latter cannot then be constant.

But this is obvious nonsense! Uranium, thorium and radium are mined as an ore; they occur in pitchblende which for millions of years has been lying in the depths of the earth. If these substances radiate to-day, they must always have radiated. But then the amount of energy they have already radiated must be staggering. 100 gramme-calories in an hour, in 24 . . . , in a year . . . , in a thousand years . . . ! The puzzle is unsolved; is it insoluble?

The few degrees rise in temperature is thus of immense importance, touching the very foundations of all previous knowledge. Everywhere Curie's experiments are checked, everywhere his results are confirmed.

In Montreal Rutherford believes in the transmutation of radio-active atoms—the ink is barely dry on his Theory of Radio-active Decay. Has he not thoroughly investigated the transmutation of thorium into thorium-X and of thorium-X into thorium emanation? Shortly after his discovery of thorium emanation, Dorn in Halle has discovered a similar gas produced by radium, and therefore called radium emanation. Rutherford believes that this highly radio-active gas also changes into other substances.

Rutherford argues thus: If radium gives off heat and if the production of heat is connected with the transmutation of its atoms one must assume that a part of the heat produced is connected with the transmutation of radium into the emanation, and the remainder of the heat with the transmutation of the emanation into other substances. Normally the emanation formed clings to the radium. Since it is, however, possible by warming or melting the compounds of radium to separate them, it should be possible to separate and distinguish their respective shares of the heat produced.

With Rutherford it is only a short distance from the idea to the experiment. The result is unambiguous: after the emanation has been separated, the heat produced by radium is only a fifth of what it was and the previous temperature is only recovered gradually as the radium produces new emanation. Only one fifth of the total heat produced is therefore attributable to the radium itself, four fifths to the emanation! A magnificent result, since the strength of the radiation of the radium which has been exhausted of emanation stands in the ratio of 1:4 to the radiation of the liberated emanation. The direct connection of the production of heat with radio-active radiation is thus proved.

Radium emanation 'lives' for only four days. Here then, we have a substance which produces heat and (probably on that account) becomes exhausted. The significance of this is clear: the energy—both the radiation and the heat produced—springs from the store of energy contained in the radio-active atoms—a great store maybe, but still a limited one. As the atoms change the energy is liberated. Thus far the problem is solved. But the radium itself? Is it inexhaustible?

Rutherford thinks not! According to his theory of decay, radium gradually changes into radium emanation, the amount of radium decreasing correspondingly. This must happen so slowly that it cannot be observed with the means available. Rutherford has still not been able to count the alpha particles of radium individually, but he has obtained an approximation to their number by measuring the total charge, and with that an approximation to the number of radium atoms decaying' per second. He finds that a given amount of radium will be reduced by half over a period of 1,000 to 2,000 years, the rest having changed into other substances via radium emanation.

The old problem still remains: if radium is transmuted completely within a few thousand years, how can it be present in uranium ore?

Rutherford's answer is that it is constantly being re-formed. Just as the emanation is a 'descendant' of radium, so too must radium be a descendant of some ancestor. But what ancestor? In nature radium always occurs with uranium, always in the same ratio to the uranium even. Radium must, therefore, be a descendant of uranium, even if only a remote one. How long does uranium radiate? Since the radiation of uranium is a million times weaker than that of radium, it must 'live' a million times longer. Uranium thus lives long enough to have existed since the beginning of the world without having yet completely disappeared.

The solution Rutherford offers is still relatively unsupported, but each passing year will bring new proof, until Rutherford's bold conception finally becomes an irrefutable certainty.

Even now, however, in 1903, the total energy produced by radium can be calculated; 100 gramme-calories per hour (exact value discovered later = 140 gramme-calories), per day . . . , per year. . . . A not too difficult calculation shows that the steadily decreasing radium emits as much energy as if the heat produced were constant for 2,000 years and then stopped suddenly. The results of the calculation show:

Each gramme of radium produces *in toto* (including the emanation and the next three products) energy equivalent to 3,000,000 kilocalories or 3,000 kilowatt-hours, or as much heat as can be obtained from 7 cwts. of coal.

This is the first calculation in figures of atomic energy. We are still in the year 1903, and half a century will pass before these figures, first scribbled on a scrap of paper, will become an exciting, breathtaking, deadly reality.

4

UNDER THE GAZE
OF MILLIARDS OF YEARS

O N 21st July 1798, in view of the pyramids, Bonaparte addressed his troops before they joined battle with the Mamelukes with the words—adapted in our heading—'Soldiers! You are under the gaze of forty centuries.'

Forty centuries, some hundred and fifty generations of mankind have passed since hordes of slaves built up the huge stone blocks into the mightiest edifices of history. Yet these forty centuries are but a trifling moment against the ages which look down on the rock itself, from which the pyramids are built. From these great blocks of granite not hundreds, not thousands, not even millions—but milliards of years look down.

Who would be rash enough to give an exact figure for the age of this diorite and granite, this gneiss and basalt? How many millions or milliards of years have passed since the formation of their tiny crystals out of a fiery, molten mass?

By comparison, it is easy for the archaeologist to date, often to within a generation, events that happened four, five, or six thousand years back. How can dates be established for ages which have left no traditions, when there were no humans living on the earth, or—going back far enough—when not even the earliest forms of life existed?

Even here there are possibilities. Thus, for instance, the age of the oceans has been tentatively calculated from the depth of the layers of sediment deposited on their bed, as the rate of deposit to-day can be gauged from observations. The amount of salt taken up from stone and carried down all the rivers of the world has also been computed, and from that has been reckoned how long the oceans would have taken to acquire their present salinity. By such computations the age of the earth's crust itself has been set at about 100 million years. But how reliable is all this? Is it known whether sediments were deposited on the ocean bed in those dim ages at the same rate as they are to-day? Is it known how much salt—or even how much water—the rivers contained then?

Some kind of clock—that would be the thing! A clock that was set going when the earth came into being, or better perhaps, when the solid crust of the earth and the various rocks were formed, and that has ticked steadily away ever since; a clock whose hands would tell us quite simply: 528 million or 1·75 milliard years ago I was set going.

We possess such clocks. They are the radio-active substances.

*　　*　　*

The knowledge that the transformation of radio-active material always takes place at a constant rate goes back to the early days of radium research. Henri Becquerel, in the first years of our century, observed that it is possible to separate from uranium by chemical means a substance, uranium-X, which is different from uranium though similarly radio-active, and whose radio-activity decreases as time passes. While only half the radio-activity of the uranium-X remains after less than a month, the uranium from which the uranium-X has been extracted 'recovers' in exactly the same period. And then came the famous experiments of Ernest Rutherford and Frederick Soddy in Montreal with thorium and thorium-X (whose relationship is similar to that of uranium and uranium-X); these showed that the thorium-X separated from thorium falls to half its radio-activity in under four days, while the thorium recovers again at the same rate. On these experiments is based the Rutherford-Soddy theory of decay: thorium changes continually into thorium-X, and this again changes into a new substance, thorium emanation. In the same way, uranium changes continually into uranium-X, and the radium emanation changes into a new substance, the so-called radium-A. And all these changes take place at a definite rate, and this rate is characteristic for each substance.

The years following the experiments of Rutherford and Soddy brought further examples of radio-active change over a period of time. They showed ever more clearly that this rate is characteristic for each radio-active substance, and that it cannot be modified or influenced in any way: radio-active decay cannot be checked or accelerated—its rate is eternal and immutable, inherent in the nature of the process. It became ever more certain —as Rutherford had intuitively realized—that this is the operation of a universal law, valid over the whole field of radio-activity.

This law states: every radio-active substance changes at a definite, constant rate, which is characteristic, into another (radio-active or non-radio-active) substance. The process is the same for all radio-active substances: when exactly half of a radio-active substance changes over a given period, then half of the remainder changes over a subsequent period of the same duration, and so on. But this means that the time in which half of any amount of a given substance changes is characteristic of that particular substance: scientists call this its *half-life*. After the duration of its half-life there remains half of a given amount of a radio-active substance, after twice its half-life one quarter, after three times its half-life one eighth, and so to infinity. The substance is *never* completely exhausted, and when we say that a substance (e.g. radium emanation) 'lives' for 4 days, we mean that its half-life is 4 days (though, strictly speaking, and for reasons we cannot go into here, we understand by the 'mean duration of life' 1·44 times the half-life). We can calculate that, even after 40 days, there remains about one thousandth of the original amount.

This, then, is how these radio-active clocks work. They do not run at a uniform rate like a watch: initially they run faster, then more slowly, and finally ever more slowly. Yet they never stop, but go on for æons.

There are, indeed, very different radio-active clocks; some are faster, some slower. There are radio-active substances with short and others with long half-lives. Even substances like radium and uranium, which at first seemed unchanging, are no exceptions to the general law. They, too, change—but only very, very slowly.

Only ten years after the pioneering work of Rutherford and Soddy it was possible to draw up a long list of radio-active substances, each with its characteristic half-life. Here is a selection from this list, arranged according to the increasing half-life:

Thorium-C′	3 ten-millionths of a second
Radium-C′	1·5 ten-thousandths of a second
Actinium emanation	3·9 seconds
Thorium emanation	54 seconds
Radium emanation	3·85 days
Uranium-X	24 days
Polonium	136 days
Radium	1,580 years
Ionium	76,000 years
Uranium	4·6 milliard years
Thorium	13·4 milliard years.

The extremely short and extremely long half-lives were known only approximately at that time, and have therefore been replaced in the list by more recent and more accurate figures.

Ten years after the pioneering discovery of Rutherford and Soddy, scientists were already busy using these radio-active clocks to date accurately the geological epochs, to measure the age of rocks—the physicist Boltwood at Yale, the geologist Holmes, and the physicist R. J. Strutt (Lord Rayleigh's son) in London.

$$\star \qquad \star \qquad \star$$

How are these radio-active clocks used? How can the duration of radio-active change be followed experimentally?

The best means of measuring radio-active substances is always their radiation, whose intensity, even when it is very weak, can be ascertained exactly. If the quantity of a substance decreases through radio-active change over a period of time, then its radiation naturally decreases by an equivalent amount. But there is a difficulty. The substance arising from the change is itself usually radio-active, so that an ever-increasing radiation from substance 2 runs parallel to the ever-diminishing radiation of substance 1. This, however, by no means implies that there is no over-all change. Substance 2 will usually emit a different kind of radiation from substance 1. Thus, for instance, if substance 1 emits only alpha rays and substance 2 only beta rays, it is an easy matter to distinguish between the rays and follow the process of change from the decrease in alpha radiation. And even when both substances emit the same kind of ray, say alpha rays, there are generally detectable differences in their penetration. For it was established quite early that each radio-active substance emits its own characteristic radiation. And so, even in these cases, a distinction can be made and the duration of the change followed.

In such ways the early research workers did, in fact, determine all the half-lives which are of convenient duration—that is, in minutes, hours, days, weeks or months. And, where it is appropriate, it is still done thus to-day. But the very short and very long half-lives require other methods; and we will consider the substances with a long half-life, as only these are relevant as geological clocks.

It has been discovered that in every radio-active change of *one* atom precisely *one* alpha particle or beta electron is thrown out. Knowing this, it is possible to measure the rate of decay per second of even those substances which decay extremely slowly: the number of alpha particles (the very slowly decaying substances almost all emit alpha rays) given off per second is determined, either by direct counting—of which interesting process we shall speak later—or simply by measuring the total electrical discharge.

Thus it is found that 1 gm. of uranium (*pure* uranium of atomic weight 238, free from all its decay products) emits some 12,000 alpha particles per second; that is, in the one gramme some 12,000 atoms change every second. A small calculation shows that it takes just 4·6 milliard years for half the 2,500 trillion atoms in one gramme of uranium to change.

And so now we can determine from the intensity of the radiation the half-life of even the most long-lived substances, like uranium and thorium—and, of course, radium. Even so, we are still far from being able to discover the *age* of the uranium ores. The radiation tells us only how the clock is going at the moment, not the whole length of time that it has been going since the uranium ore, which we now have in our hands, first emerged as a solid fragment from the molten mass of the young earth. It is not as simple as that, and so we must look about for other ways of reading the radio-active clocks.

We ask ourselves: what remains after one of these radio-active changes? Naturally, the substance produced by the change. This is usually radio-active as well, and decays in its turn. But let us consider the case of a radio-active substance that simply changes into one that is not radio-active, that is 'stable' (there are, in fact, a few such simple changes). Here the new substance 2 accumulates in the same measure as substance 1 disappears. It is very like the sand-glass that the housewife uses as an egg-timer. The amount of sand at the bottom is the measure of the time that has passed since the glass was inverted. In the same way, the amount of substance 2 that has accumulated over millions of years is the measure of the time that has passed since. . . . Well, since when? Clearly, since the substance in question became *solid*. For, so long as it was liquid, the newly-formed substances were continually being removed by currents or by mixing. But they can no longer escape from the solid fragment; very slowly they accumulate. Millions of years are but a day to them. At last the fragment falls into the hands of a chemist; he analyses it—reads the sand-glass—and says: thus much of substance 2 has accumulated, and accordingly so many millions or milliards of years have passed since this fragment solidified.

So we come near the solution of the problem. And yet— uranium or thorium, which are of first importance heee, do not change into a non-radio-active, stable substance 2, which could accumulate. They become substances—uranium-X or thorium-X (the latter actually by intermediate stages), which themselves decay in their turn!

But it is not as bad as it seems. Surely something stable must eventually be left. Hence the vital question is: how, after what pattern, do the radio-active substances change the one into the other? Do stable substances, which no longer decay, finally result? And what sort of substances are they?

A great part of the research on radio-activity in the first decade of this century did indeed centre upon these questions. And the answers to them, slowly emerging more plainly out of an initially confusing abundance of individual observations, present a new and fascinating picture of impressively compact simplicity.

★　　★　　★

When Rutherford and Soddy propounded their theory of decay in 1902 it implied an extensive programme. The outlines of the new conceptions had to be filled in with specific examples of radio-active change. A certain, limited amount was already known, and this was the starting-point of the theory of decay; thereafter the way led into unexplored territory.

It was known, for instance, that thorium-X is formed from thorium, thorium emanation from thorium-X. It was known that uranium changes into uranium-X, radium into radium emanation, actinium into actinium emanation. From the emanations, again, arise new solid substances, likewise radio-active—the 'active deposits', which can soon be analysed into several new substances.

And so whole series of substances can be distinguished, of which each is formed from a preceding one through radio-active decay. Whole radio-active family-trees were investigated, and the physicists of this time were rather like genealogists penetrating the complex relationships of the members of a large family—which are not always obvious. Publications abounded with phrases like 'presumably there is an intermediate stage between this and that substance' or 'the genetic relationship between these substances would appear to be such and such'. Sometimes the assumptions were later proved wrong, and ideas had to be revised. Generally, however, the assumptions, through the gradual accumulation of conclusive evidence, became certainties.

The genealogical table of radium soon appeared thus (half-life in brackets): radium (1,580 years)—radium emanation (4 days)—radium-A (3 minutes)—radium-B (27 minutes)—radium-C (20 minutes)—radium-C' (1·5 ten-thousandths of a second)—radium-D (25 years)—radium-E (5 days)—radium-F or polonium (136 days)—radium G.

Polonium, then, the element discovered by Marie Curie *before* radium, proves to be a descendant of radium. But what is this radium-G? Why does the chain break off here?—Because the changes end here, and the radium-G emits no radiation; it is not radio-active, but a *stable* substance. The change of polonium into radium-G is an example of those simple changes. Radium-G is a substance which no longer decays, and so can accumulate unhindered. Surely, then, it must be present in some quantity in radium-bearing minerals. Can it be found there?

The physical chemist from Yale University in New Haven, U.S.A., Bertram Borden Boltwood, a friend of Rutherford's, was the first to suspect (in 1905) that this radium-G is nothing but—lead. Lead occurs in all uranium ores, from which radium is extracted. In time, this suspicion was proved true. Yet it is not ordinary lead, this end-product of the radium decay series. Calculations from the number of alpha particles emitted by one radium atom (through the series) show that this lead should have an atomic weight of 206, whereas 'ordinary' lead, as it occurs naturally, has an atomic weight of 207·2. In 1914 the Austrian chemists Otto Hönigschmid and Stephanie Horovitz found that lead out of uranium ore from St. Joachimsthal in Bohemia does, in fact, have an atomic weight of 206·7, and some from Morogoro in East Africa actually has the exact atomic weight of 206·0. Thus the circle of proof closed.

But where does this long-lived radium itself, the starting-point of the series, come from? As it is found only in uranium ores, it seemed clear that it must also derive from uranium. Yet uranium changes into uranium-X, which decays with a half-life of 24 days; so the scientists vainly investigated it to seek the expected new formation from radium. It seemed that another, very long-lived and weakly radio-active, intermediate product is interposed, which obscures the relationship. So began the search for 'the father of radium'. Once more it was Boltwood who succeeded (in 1907), just before Otto Hahn, who at this time was also hard on the heels of 'the father of radium'. Boltwood discovered ionium, with a half-life of nearly 100,000 years, which changes into radium. Thus the genetic relationship between uranium and radium was clarified, though later further intermediate stages were discovered, which we cannot discuss here.

Similar series to that of uranium start with thorium and actinium. The three radio-active decay series were talked about —the uranium-radium series, the thorium series and the actinium series, together comprising almost all known radio-active substances, which numbered at this time, ten years after the Rutherford-Soddy theory of decay, about 30 (to-day about 50).

With the completion of the thorium series we again meet Otto Hahn, now in Berlin; his name will recur from the moment he first appeared as a young man with Rutherford in Montreal until his world-shaking discovery marks the zenith of his career in 1938. As early as 1905 Hahn had brought to Montreal the discovery of radio-thorium, an intermediate product between thorium and thorium-X, and had there conclusively established its existence. Now in Berlin he found two further intermediate products, mesothorium 1 and mesothorium 2, the former of which, with its relatively long half-life of seven years, was soon produced industrially and began to play a part in the clinical treatment of cancer.

Again, during the war in 1917, Hahn made yet another important discovery, together with Lise Meitner, who worked with him for over thirty years, and who had remained at the Hahn Institute in Berlin, where she had come from Vienna in 1907 to complete her training. Hahn and Lise Meitner discovered protactinium, the link between uranium and actinium. Thus actinium and the whole actinium series also belong with uranium; though, as later became apparent, not with normal uranium of atomic weight 238, but with a special uranium of atomic weight 235, which occurs in small quantities in natural uranium. This uranium 235, originally of only scientific interest as the progenitor of the actinium series, was destined to produce the explosion in the first atomic bomb.

The starting-point of nearly all the radio-active materials then known (a few others, of very low radio-activity, like potassium and rubidium, which do not belong to any of the three series, were also known) is natural uranium and natural thorium. What are the end-products? In the case of radium (and hence of uranium 238) it is, as we have seen, lead of atomic weight 206; in the case of actinium (and hence of uranium 235) it again turns out to be lead, but this time with an atomic weight of 207, almost the same as common lead. And thorium finally gives lead of atomic weight 208: all the radio-active substances of the three decay series end in lead.

But how can lead have three different atomic weights? Why is there uranium of atomic weight 238 and 235? Is it not part of the definition of the atom that every element has its own distinct kind of atom with *one* specific atomic weight? And is it not true that the chemists—until this confusion is introduced by radio-activity—have found for each element only *one* atomic weight, which is invariable and which, in many instances, has been accurately determined to three decimal places?

Obviously there was something new here. The conception of the atom needed revising, and this was the point at which it must be altered. The conception of *isotopes* now came into the field of vision of the radium workers, a conception of prime importance, which radically modified future developments. But the reader must be patient for a while, until the isotopes, introduced by their discoverer, Frederick Soddy, make their official entry into this drama.

★   ★   ★

Though every detail was still not clear, various scientists set to work after 1905 to establish the age of the rocks and of the geological epochs by means of the radio-active clocks. Once more the first in the field was the American, Boltwood, who tested uranium-bearing rock for its lead content (assuming that all the lead present derived from the radio-active change of uranium), and so deduced the age of the rocks. Later the London geologist Holmes extended the tests to a great variety of rocks, analysing for their lead content specimens from all parts of the world and from all geological epochs. And there is no need to restrict the tests solely to actual uranium ores. Many, indeed nearly all, the rocks of the earth's crust contain a small admixture of uranium minerals, and this suffices to establish their ages.

It was not long before the earlier estimates of 100 million years were proved to be far too low. A uranite from the Carboniferous Age, from a Cambrian formation, in which the plant and animal kingdoms were already highly developed, gives a result of 340 million years. With the middle pre-Cambrian the milliard years is reached, and the oldest rocks from the Black Hills of South Dakota and from Finnish Karelia show 1·5, 1·8 and 2 milliard years. Similarly, it is possible to work out these ages from thorium: they correspond essentially with the others.

Yet there is one consideration that may raise our doubts. How can we know that *all* the lead found in association with uranium or thorium has actually been produced by radio-active decay? Perhaps the rocks contained ordinary lead from their origins in the molten mass—and if this is included as being a radio-active product, then the resultant age will be far too great. The necessity presents itself of being able to differentiate between lead produced by radio-activity and common lead.

This soon became possible. Lead deriving from uranium has an atomic weight of 206, and that from thorium one of 208, whereas the atomic weight of common lead is 207·2. Since Hönigschmid accurately determined the atomic weights, it is possible to say whether all the lead in any given specimen is of radio-active origin. In very many cases this method has shown that all the lead in a sample does indeed derive from uranium or thorium. In those cases where ordinary lead is also present, the necessary corrections can be made to the results.

From the beginning another method has competed with these computations based on the lead content. The alpha particles emitted by radio-active uranium and thorium and their serial products are charged helium atoms. In the course of time, therefore, helium gas is formed, most of which remains 'occluded' in the rock; and the amount thus enclosed can be determined by analysis. The London physicist R. J. Strutt* developed the 'helium method', which permits the calculation of the age of rocks from the amount of helium that has accreted between the dim past and our own day.

So the researches on the primeval period of the world progressed. In later years we come upon Otto Hahn again—just before his great discovery of uranium splitting: with other scientists (among them Fritz Strassmann), he introduced a new method—the determination of geological age by means of the strontium formed from radio-active rubidium. Most recently have been added the use of argon formed from radio-active potassium and of osmium from radio-active rhenium.

Now there are a number of independent possibilities. They

* Later the fourth Baron Rayleigh; his father, the third Baron, was a well-known physicist, who helped to discover the inert gas argon and was a Nobel Prize winner in 1904.

all provide mutual confirmation of their results. The geological ages, whose sequence alone had previously been established, can now be dated accurately. It is some 150 million years since the Jurassic ocean deposited its sediments, 300 million years since the primeval forests of horsetails of the Carboniferous Age, 600 million years since the appearance of the earliest classifiable invertebrates, 1·2 milliard years since the beginning of the middle pre-Cambrian Age, and over 2 milliard years since the first rocks solidified out of the molten mass that was the world in its infancy. The 'mere' 100,000 years allowed for the existence of the human race make no very impressive showing in this time-table of æons, of which they represent only the last twenty-thousandth part.

As the time between the splitting-off the earth and all the other planets from the sun and the solidification of the earth cannot have been very long—the outer crust of the earth cools fairly rapidly—the age of the earth works out at around three milliard years. For a long time this stood in contradiction to cosmic calculations, according to which the age of the entire universe was believed to be hardly two milliard years. But the information obtained with the new giant telescope on Mount Palomar in California has caused a revision of these calculations. The age of the cosmos is now reckoned to be at least four milliard years, so that the discrepancy with the computation of the earth's age is eliminated. Nevertheless, the comment of the late Richard Gans to his students in Königsberg, after explaining how the age of the earth is calculated, has not lost all its point: 'The age of the world is like that of a pretty woman. It is not necessarily the right one.'

*   *   *

The pyramids of Gizeh introduced this chapter; and they shall conclude it. From the millions and milliards of years of the geological ages we return again to those modest thousands which concern the archaeologist, to the tombs of the Pharaohs, to the ruins of Nineveh, or the abandoned jungle cities of the Mayas. We return to find that here, too, the radio-active clocks have been functioning, throwing new light on scarcely-suspected facts of historical time.

The story of this scientific achievement is set, as recently as 1948, in the University of Chicago, and its hero is the American chemist Willard Frank Libby, who was born in the state of Colorado in the year of Becquerel's death (1908), when the lead and helium methods had already brought their first results in connection with the geological ages.

Yet how should radio-active clocks, set going hundreds of millions, or even milliards of years ago, now suddenly register a few thousand years; how should they tell us how long an Egyptian king has been resting in his grave? Obviously it cannot be done by the same clocks. It is, indeed, a much more recently discovered radio-active material that performs the new miracle: and this material is—carbon. But not the ordinary carbon that has been known since the distant past, to which chemists have long ago ascribed the atomic weight 12; it is a strangely *different*, radio-active carbon, an 'isotope' of ordinary carbon, having an atomic weight of 14, which is referred to briefly as C 14.

The facts about this carbon are strange. Much that is new had to be discovered before C 14 could become a radio-active clock in Libby's hands; and first we ought really to discuss many other things (which will be dealt with more fully later), among them the isotopes, artificial radiation, cosmic rays, and much else. Even so, we can indicate what happens.

It is common knowledge that our atmosphere contains carbon dioxide gas (CO_2)—a combination of carbon and oxygen. It contains only a very little, about 0·03%. Yet all organic life, human, animal and vegetable, draws its sustenance directly or indirectly from it. Our atmosphere also contains nitrogen, which makes up some 80% of it. The atmosphere is continually bombarded from outer space by radiation that is of very small intensity, but whose individual particles possess extremely great energy—the so-called cosmic rays. These (more exactly, the neutrons they produce) occasionally transform an atom of nitrogen in the upper layers of the atmosphere into a radio-active carbon atom, an N 14 atom into a C 14 atom, and the C 14 combines with oxygen that is always present to form a radio-active carbonic acid, which then mixes everywhere with the ordinary carbonic acid.

The C 14 in the radio-active carbonic acid decays radio-actively with a half-life of about 5,600 years—very slowly, it is true, but still there would be practically none of it left after a few thousand years, were it not continually being replaced through the action of the cosmic rays. And so a balance between decay and replacement is established, and in every litre of ordinary carbonic acid that the air contains there is a minute amount of radio-active carbonic acid. The amount is extremely small (and, moreover, everywhere the same, because it is well mixed by the wind)—about two molecules of radio-active carbonic acid to a billion ordinary ones, so that it cannot be weighed with even the most sensitive scales, though sensitive instruments can nonetheless detect it by its radiation.

Every blade of grass, building its cell-tissues by assimilating the carbonic acid from the air, every cow eating the grass and every person who eats its meat (or eats the vegetation itself) will also have absorbed with the carbon, which makes up a large part of the substance of the body, those two billionths of radio-active carbon. Its slow decay is continually made good by its exchange for fresh carbonic acid or fresh food. But, Libby wonders, what happens when the living body—or even a single cell from it—dies.

Then assimilation and metabolism cease, no fresh C 14 is absorbed, and the established balance is replaced by the uncompensated decay of the existing store of C 14 according to its own immutable law: the radio-active clock begins to function!

After 2,000 or 4,000 or 6,000 years a scientist can read from the C 14 of the remains, from the intensity of the continuing beta radiation, how many years ago this remnant—and the living creature it represents—passed out of the ever-flowing stream of life. That is the foundation of Libby's method of assessing the age of archaeological objects.

The favourite material for investigation is wood: wood from a tree-trunk sunk in the marsh, wood from a primitive, age-old drinking vessel, charcoal from the site of a prehistoric fire, wood from the coffin of a Sumerian king, from the sun-ship of the Pharaoh. Naturally the C 14 radio-active clock does not indicate the time at which the wood was fashioned, but the time at which it was felled, or even when it died on the living tree and was cut off from the flow of sap. But these differences of a decade or so are trivial against the thousands of years involved.

And how accurate can it be in general? Is this method of determining age by radio-activity really reliable? Libby has no difficulty in testing it. There are enough old objects whose age has been established (to within a few decades) by purely archaeological means. These are the first to be tackled. It is known that the cypress beams in the grave of king Sneferu at Meydum are 4,575 years old (to within 75 years). The C 14 says 4,800 years. The archaeologists give the age of the burial-ship of king Sesostris III as 3,750 years. The C 14 says 3,620 years. Examples multiply; and where reliable ages are already available, the C 14 method has shown at least an approximate agreement.

Indeed, owing to the great difficulty of measuring the weak beta radiation, it is not very exact. An error of at least 100-200 years must be allowed. Its results are always inferior to reliable archaeological assessments of age based on historical material.

Nevertheless, the new territory opened up is immense; only a few years before, its penetration must have seemed hopeless. Now an object of wood or charcoal or any other organic material which is found unrelated to any known culture, can be dated with some degree of certainty. Everywhere the radio-active clocks of the C 14 are ticking noiselessly away, casting a net of time over the last 20,000 years of human history.

5

THE NUCLEUS ACHIEVES RECOGNITION

WHEN Rutherford published his calculations concerning atoms, with a charge concentrated in a point at the centre and having mass, in the *Philosophical Magazine* for May 1911, few people realised that this represented a signal advance in modern physics. The views expressed in the article were in direct conflict with the popular conception of the atom, as propounded by J. J. Thomson—a conception which continued to enjoy the support of most physicists even after Rutherford's views were published.

J. J. Thomson saw the atom as a relatively large sphere with a positive charge in which electrons are located, rather like currants in a cake. These electrons, which vary in number according to the nature of the atom, compensate exactly the positive charge of the sphere (the atom as a whole is electrically neutral) and form within the atom a stable pattern in which they rotate.

Rutherford had rejected Thomson's model atom, since this conception could not explain why a few of the many alpha particles which strike the atom are deflected from their course while most of them pass through unhindered—a fact established by the experiments of Geiger and Marsden. Rutherford's postulation of an atom which has mass which is concentrated in the centre—the postulation of an atomic nucleus in fact—would explain the deflection of an alpha particle when the particle strikes a tiny but massive nucleus more or less directly. The experimentally measurable angle of deflection of the alpha particle agreed admirably with the result of the calculations based on Rutherford's postulation.

Rutherford's conclusions were compelling, but it is understandable that the unconventional picture of the new model atom, which presents considerable difficulties in the explanation of the stability of the electrons grouped around the nucleus, was not accepted immediately—the question of the 'construction' of the atom was so new and so heretical compared with the previous conception of 'indivisibility'. Concrete experimental proofs were needed to make this idea, which at first lacked firm foundations, generally acceptable. The atomic nucleus, with which the physicists had, unbeknown to themselves, been occupied for fifteen years now, the nucleus first recognized in Rutherford's bold postulation, had to struggle for a few more years before achieving final recognition.

In 1911 Rutherford deduced from Geiger's experimental results the size of the charge of the nucleus of a given atom, and discovered that this charge, when expressed in multiples of the elementary charge—the charge of one electron—is roughly equivalent to half the atomic weight of that atom. Accordingly the nucleus of an atom of iron—atomic weight 56—must have a total charge of 28 elementary charges (to-day we know it to be 26); the nucleus of a carbon atom—atomic weight 12—one of 6 elementary charges; the nucleus of a helium atom (which is nothing but an alpha particle)—atomic weight 4—will have the two elementary charges long ascribed to it. Only in the case of hydrogen does this rule not apply. Here the atomic weight is 1 and the nuclear charge is obviously also 1 elementary charge. The hydrogen nucleus, the most simple of all nuclei, was later called the proton and played a great part in subsequent developments.

Can anything be said about the number of electrons surrounding the nucleus? In the neutral atom the number of electrons must equal the number of positive elementary charges in the nucleus—therefore the iron atom must have 26, that of carbon 6, that of helium 2 and that of hydrogen 1. And how do we know that the negative 'shell' of the atom is made up of electrons? When any type of atom is bombarded with electrons from another atom, or is subjected to ultra-violet radiation, one, two, or possibly more electrons are dislodged, leaving a simple group of positive ions, singly, doubly or multiply charged positive ions, which have in their negative 'shell' one, two, or more electrons too few, so that the positive charge of the nucleus is no longer fully compensated.

It is also possible to determine the number of electrons by the degree to which X-rays are scattered when passed through a substance made up of a given type of atom. Since it is the electrons which are responsible for this 'scattering', it is possible to calculate from it the number of electrons by applying a theory of J. J. Thomson's. This theory is independent of the actual distribution of the electrons and is still valid to-day. Professor C. G. Barkla of King's College, London, had attempted in 1904 to calculate the number of the electrons in this way, but had met with little success in view of the uncertain data on the mass and charges of electrons. Simultaneously with Rutherford's investigations, Barkla now made new calculations and found that the number of electrons, except in the case of hydrogen, is roughly equal to half the atomic weight. Strangely enough his results were published in the same number of the *Philosophical Magazine* as Rutherford's calculations on the atomic nucleus. Only a few pages separate Barkla's equation of the number of electrons with half the atomic weight and Rutherford's equation of the nuclear charge with half the atomic weight. Yet both approached the problem from different sides. In view of the electrical neutrality of the atom, however, it follows that the number of electrons equals the number of elementary nuclear charges.

In April of the same year, van den Broek sent an article to the *Physical Journal* in which he attempted to integrate the numerous newly discovered radio-active elements into the periodic table of chemical elements. The attempt was practically a failure, but in November 1912 he met with greater success. In the course of a careful examination of the whole periodic system, he discovered that the number given to the element by its position in the periodic table is identical with the number of electrons and the number of elementary charges. That iron in the periodic table has the number 26 also means that its atom has 26 electrons and its nucleus 26 elementary charges.

Thus more and more proof was found for the correctness of Rutherford's model atom. The scepticism of contemporaries began to weaken and slowly the concept of the nucleus gained currency. But still, even for Rutherford's disciples, the nucleus was only a massive electrically charged particle, which formed the centre of the atom. No one yet realized the powers it contained or that it would soon be the subject of a special branch of science—nuclear physics.

*   *   *

One thing was already clear: the nucleus is responsible for the great majority of radio-active processes.

The changes taking place in radio-active substances must obviously be mutations of the nucleus, since the latter determines by the size of its charge how many electrons make up the atom, and thereby determines the chemical nature of the atom itself.

As far as the radiations emitted by the radio-active substances in the course of their mutations are concerned, at least the alpha particles can only originate in the nucleus, since all the electrons of even the heaviest atom taken together have barely more than $\frac{1}{100}$ the mass of one alpha particle. Rutherford believed that beta and gamma rays originate in the encasing electrons, but soon it proved that nuclear processes are concerned in these too and that the beta and gamma rays also originate in the nucleus and are independent of the electrons.

The significance is clear: atomic nuclei are not indivisible units. They change into other nuclei, and in the process emit particles in the form of rays—they are composed of tiny particles no greater in size than the thousandth part of an atom! The discovery of the nucleus thus only solved in part the problem of the construction of an atom, and threw up the problem of the construction of the nucleus.

Further, a simple calculation shows that the 'binding energy', the energy responsible for the attraction of the electrons to the nucleus, is grossly insufficient to account for the vast energy present in radio-active materials. This vast reserve of energy must therefore lie in the nucleus.

The description of the atom as it appeared in 1890 which we gave above now needs certain modifications. The atom can no longer be regarded as indivisible. The atom does continue to be regarded as the smallest particle in a chemical element, for the known chemical properties apply to the atom as an undivided whole, but it is certainly not indivisible, and this sentence in our description must now be amended to read: each atom consists of a central nucleus with a positive charge, which comprises almost the whole of the mass of the atom, and a number of encasing electrons.

In the case of a whole, undivided, electrically neutral atom the number of elementary charges in the nucleus is the same as that of the encasing electrons. This figure is the same as the periodic number of the element of which the atom is made, and in the lighter elements is roughly equal to half the atomic weight. The periodic number and the number of elementary charges in the nucleus remain equal when the electrons round the nucleus are removed, by which process the atom is converted into a positive ion of the given element. The individual parts of the atom have various functions in the physical processes associated with the atom. The electrons are responsible for the emission and absorption of light and X-rays, and for the ability of the atoms to collect in molecules—i.e. for the chemical properties of the atom. The nucleus is responsible for the radio-active processes, for mutations and radiations.

The electrons are attached to the nucleus by electrical forces, and a certain energy is needed to detach them from it. The energy present in radio-active radiations originates from a mysterious store of energy in the nucleus. The energy contained in the nucleus is millions of times greater than the chemical energies which spring from changes in the pattern of the encasing electrons. In the case of radio-active energy, and later in the case of the energy liberated by artificial nuclear mutation, it is more correct to speak of nuclear energy than of atomic energy.

Although they are only about 1/100,000 of a millimetre in size, the nuclei of radio-active atoms are themselves composed of particles about which nothing is known. Nor is it known whether the nuclei of the more stable non-radio-active atoms are made up of particles, or in what way they are constructed.

Finally we shall be able to delete from our description of the atom as it appeared in 1890 the question as to whether the atom does actually exist—in view of the incontrovertible experimental results, this can no longer be questioned.

Now we must turn our attention to certain highly important events in the world of physics which occurred in the first decade of our century—events not directly concerned with the science of radio-activity, but which will later make important contributions to this branch of physics.

★   ★   ★

During the twenty years from 1913 to 1933 the Berlin Society was fortunate in having amongst its members two theoretical physicists who shook the prevailing view of the physical world to its very foundations, two men who worked side by side and were in addition linked by their common love of music and by the bonds of friendship: Max Planck and Albert Einstein.

It would be difficult to imagine two more different personalities —Planck, twenty-one years Einstein's senior, a lean man with sharp features, cold penetrating eyes behind his rimless spectacles, his sparse hair combed straight back; Einstein, powerful, almost comfortable in appearance, a soft friendly face framed by a wild mane of hair;—Planck, a man of sober and precise diction, bred in the atmosphere of the university, careful and conservative, an enemy of all exaggeration; Einstein, more of an artist by nature, a lover of radical statements, a man of scientific passion. To an observer it would appear that Einstein was more capable of evolving some revolutionary theory than Planck. Yet Planck's Quantum Theory is one whose subsequent development shook the prevailing conceptions of the scientific world perhaps even more radically than Einstein's Theory of Relativity.

Both men had made their most signal contribution to knowledge before they met in Berlin—Planck as professor of theoretical physics in Berlin, and Einstein as a petty official in the Swiss patent office in Bern.

In purely experimental physics the nineteenth century had done good work and a whole host of remarkable scientific discoveries heralded the approach of the new century. Hertz's waves, radium, and the free electron shook the old world of physics to its foundations. On the theoretical side, almost as soon as the free electron had been discovered, the great Hendrik Antoon Lorentz had evolved an astounding theory of the nature of electrons which to-day is still found to be correct.

One of the greatest problems at the turn of the century was the theory of the radiation of heat and light, emitted by a heated body, which in the hollow cavity of that body obeys certain simple laws. Physicists spoke, therefore, of 'cavity radiation'. Famous men, like Lord Rayleigh and Willi Wien, had devoted their attention to this problem and had arrived at formulae intended to show how the energy of cavity radiation is spread by the various radiation frequencies—in the case of light we speak of colour—it contains. Unfortunately these formulae did not agree with each other or with experimental results.

Still, the two formulae must be right to some extent. Rayleigh's formula agreed with empirical results as far as definite heat radiation at low frequencies was concerned, but was useless when applied to high frequencies. Wien's formula, on the other hand, agreed with empirical results at high frequencies, but was inapplicable to low frequencies. Both formulae were useless when applied to medium frequencies. Yet there seemed no way of arriving at formulae other than these.

Max Planck was destined to cut the Gordian knot. In a memorable session of the Berlin Physical Society on 19th October 1900, during which Rubens and Kurlbaum had reported on their new and exact measurements of cavity radiation, Planck made known a radiation formula which covered the experimental results at all frequencies. Planck's radiation formula had only one blemish—at the moment it was the result of inspired intuition rather than of theoretical deduction.

The theoretical proof of the theory was laid before the Society a bare two months later, on 14th December 1900. What Planck had to say was more than strange. He introduced assumptions which contradicted everything which had previously been regarded as firmly established. He maintained that the radiation of energy of an electro-mechanical system, of an atom, for instance, was not a continuous process but that the atom emitted energy *in quanta* (i.e. discontinuously), for the size of which Planck could actually produce figures. In compelling fashion he showed that only when this assumption was made in the theoretical deductions could the correct radiation formula be obtained.

The idea was too revolutionary to meet with immediate

acceptance, and like many great theories had to wait for years before meeting complete acceptance.

At this time, Albert Einstein was only twenty-one years old. He had just completed his physics course at the Technische Hochschule in Zürich and entered upon his career. First he taught and then moved to the Patent Office in Bern. But in the year 1905 this obscure young man published no less than four articles in the *Annals of Physics*. In the first article Planck's Quantum Theory is developed in an important way. Einstein attributes to the quanta of the radiation of light (and similar radiations) an independent existence; he introduces the concept of light quanta and radiation quanta into physics. The second article propounds a theory of the so-called 'Brownian movement', the slight trembling movement of tiny particles of dust suspended in a liquid or a gas as a result of the jostling of the molecules. The two final articles, however, conceal under the modest titles, 'On the electro-dynamics of moving bodies' and 'Is the inertia of a body dependent on its energy content?' a theory of immense importance—the Theory of Relativity.

★   ★   ★

We are here concerned with the Quantum Theory and the Theory of Relativity only in so far as they are of importance in the development of nuclear physics. In 1912 their significance for the nucleus itself was not yet realized, but their importance for radio-active radiation was apparent.

Take gamma rays for instance. Like light and X-rays they are waves, but have a much shorter wave-length and therefore a higher frequency. In all radiations in this group the frequency becomes higher as the wave-length becomes shorter. The wave-length multiplied by the frequency gives the speed of light. By diffraction experiments the wave-length can be measured and so the frequency calculated. In normal visible light the frequency is a few hundred billion Hertz (Hz = vibrations per second), in ordinary X-rays a few trillion and in gamma rays 200 trillion. Even to-day these tremendously high frequencies have never been measured—they are the result of calculations only.

Planck's quantum theory, developed by Einstein in 1905,

demands that the size of the energy quanta which are radiated, the size of the radiation quanta, travelling in the radiation itself at the speed of light, shall be proportional to the frequency. Visible light thus has relatively small radiation quanta, those of X-rays being a few 10,000 times greater, and those of gamma rays a few 100,000 times greater than the quanta of light. The quanta of gamma rays must thus be more easily recognizable than those of light, and indeed gamma rays were the first radiation whose quanta were counted individually.

A single gamma quantum can have energy up to 1/600,000 of an erg, i.e. the same energy as an electron accelerated through a discharge tube by a potential of one million volts. Thus we speak of gamma rays of one million electron-volts (1 M.e.v.). It is only on account of the quantum theory that we can make such a statement, since it was responsible for the knowledge that gamma rays (like X-rays and light) are not only waves, but are corpuscular in character, consisting of quanta travelling in *almost* the same way as electrons in beta rays and helium ions in alpha rays. But only almost. The quanta, soon to be called photons, are not material particles like electrons or helium ions. They are, in a very definite sense, more transitory than the latter; they arise and disappear continuously. Only the greatness of their energy may be fully compared with the kinetic energy of material particles.

Gamma rays of radio-active substances have 'quantum energy' of up to 4 M.e.v.

The electrons of radio-active beta rays have kinetic energy of up to 4 M.e.v.

The energy of alpha particles may be as high as 9 M.e.v., e.g. in the alpha rays of thorium-C'.

But the theory of relativity also has its application to the alpha and beta rays. Einstein maintains: If a material body moves so quickly that its speed becomes comparable to the speed of light (practically speaking this can only happen in the case of atom particles, electrons, etc.) its mass ceases to be constant but increases as the speed increases. According to Einstein's formula, when a mass reaches the speed of light it must become infinitely large. This cannot actually happen, and so we may say that no body can ever fully reach the speed of light, no matter how great its energy may be. The school formula $\frac{1}{2}mv^2$ for the kinetic energy of a body moving at the speed v is thus inapplicable to very high speeds and is replaced by a more complicated one.

This thesis was put to the test by several scientists, including Walter Kaufmann of Bonn, and it was shown by measuring the speed and energy of radio-active beta rays that such an increase in mass does take place. The experiments were difficult, but the validity of Einstein's formula became ever more plain. High speed electrons no longer have the same mass as when at rest or when moving at moderate speeds. Propelled by an energy of 0·1 M.e.v. they move at 55% the speed of light and their mass has increased by 20%. At 1 M.e.v. they move at 94% the speed of light and their mass has increased threefold. At 3 M.e.v. beta electrons reach 99% the speed of light and are seven times as massive as when at rest.

Alpha particles also increase in mass, but since they travel much more slowly (even when provided with greater kinetic energy) this increase is only slight.

The influence of the Theory of Relativity was not limited to the increase in mass of high-speed particles, but culminated in an all-embracing application which was to bring the whole of the world of nuclear physics under its spell.

*   *   *

Before the turn of the century H. A. Lorentz in Leiden had deduced theoretically that an electron must, simply because it is electrically charged, show inertia and consequently mass. Could the whole mass of the electron be electro-magnetic in nature? The question could not be answered then, but a link had been forged between the energy of a body and its inertia, its mass.

In 1904 the Austrian physicist, Hasenöhrl, took up the question of the connection between energy and mass. He discovered that a cavity full of radiation must, because of the radiation it contained, have a greater mass. Thus he established a connection between the energy of the radiation and a certain increase in mass, which came very near to the truth.

Undoubtedly further developments would have given the final correct formula, had not the Theory of Relativity solved the problem in general terms in 1905. Einstein's theorem said: 'All energy has mass', a theorem which led to the famous formula $E = mc^2$ for the connection between the energy E and the mass m belonging to it.

What does this mean? Crudely expressed it means that energy as well as matter weighs something. We have already seen that electricity weighs something, the electrons (its smallest particles) have mass and can be measured accurately and can be expressed in figures. But now it seems that light, heat, and kinetic energy weigh something as well! The fact that kinetic energy weighs something gains concrete expression in the increase in mass of rapidly moving particles, and so the circle closes in what is apparently an entirely different group of phenomena. But it also means that every mass represents, as mass, a certain amount of energy irrespective of whether it moves or contains energy as a result of its heat content or electrical charge. And we get the energy E which is represented by the mass m from the formula $E = mc^2$, multiplying the mass by the square of the speed of light.

In other words, we have a lump of iron weighing 1 kilogramme. We multiply its mass—i.e. 1—by the square of the speed of light, which for convenience we express in metres per second, i.e. 300 million m./sec. The square of this is 90,000 billion. This multiplied by 1 represents the energy in watt seconds. 90,000 billion watt seconds equal 25 milliard kilowatt hours. Taking a k.w.h. as being worth fourpence to the domestic consumer, our humble lump of iron thus has energy worth approximately £420,000,000. The market value of a lump of gold of the same size is as nothing compared to such a figure! If Einstein's formula is correct, each kilogramme of matter, be it stone, water, or air contains this fantastic amount of energy!

But there is a snag—the energy cannot be harnessed. According to Einstein, every kilogramme of matter represents 25 milliard k.w.h. of energy, yet obviously this cannot be transformed spontaneously or artificially into other forms of useful energy: into radiation, heat, or electrical energy. Or might it be possible? Are there not the radio-active materials, feeding their mysterious radiation from a huge store of internal energy? Is there here a practical example for the formula $E = mc^2$?

Let us consider: according to Einstein, 1 kilogramme of radium, like any other substance, contains 25 milliard k.w.h. of energy. The experiments and calculations of the Curies, of Rutherford and others have shown that 1 gramme of radium in the course of its 'life' (including the radium emanation and the three following products) gives out a total of 3,000 k.w.h. of energy in the form of radiation. Together with the further decay products right down to lead, it amounts to some 4,000 k.w.h. This gives 4 million k.w.h. per kilogramme. Great though this energy is, it is still only about one six-thousandth of the total mass energy.

Thus are stored, according to the formula $E = mc^2$, in every kind of substance, non-radio-active as well as radio-active, unimaginably huge quantities of energy. In rare instances—the radio-active substances—a small part of this energy seeps out in the form of radiation. Staggering though these amounts of atomic energy may be, they nonetheless represent a mere fraction of the mass energy of these substances.

And this raises another question. If the radio-active materials lose part of their energy through radiation, do they also lose a corresponding proportion of their mass? Clearly, the radio-active substances lose the inert mass of the alpha and beta particles they emit. But the question goes further: does the mass of the radio-active substances decrease over and above this by reason of the *energy* radiated? Obviously this must be so, as the relation between mass and energy always holds good. Hence the amount of energy given out as radiation must take with it the mass appropriate to it.

Einstein drew this conclusion from the very first. At the end of his last work (in 1905) he says: 'It is not impossible that the theory may be successfully tested in the case of bodies whose energy content is extremely variable, e.g. of the radium compounds.'

From this moment the formula $E = mc^2$ constantly accompanies radio-active research and its later development, nuclear physics. Einstein's prophecy was realized only many years afterwards—but then to an extent he never dreamed of. Out of the whole theory of relativity, the formula $E = mc^2$ became the one most thoroughly established by experiment. The formula $E = mc^2$

governs the processes of radio-active decay; it governs the processes of artificial nuclear transmutation. And finally it governs
man's most terrible incursion into the processes of nature: the
atom bomb.

★   ★   ★

But still the idea of the nucleus was not universally accepted.
It is 1912, and the single year since Rutherford's brilliant conception has not sufficed to overcome all conservative opposition
to it. Many are convinced, but some remain obstinately sceptical.

Among the enthusiastically convinced is a young Dane, who
has come to Rutherford in the early spring of 1912. Having
graduated in Copenhagen, he has just been working for six
months with J. J. Thomson in the Cavendish Laboratory. Now
he has gone to Rutherford in Manchester. His name is Niels
Bohr.

This young man is not content merely to admire Rutherford's
conception. He sets himself to develop it further. He is certain
of the existence of the nucleus; from this it follows that there
must be an appropriate number of electrons arranged around the
nucleus. But *how* are they arranged? In positions of static
equilibrium, as J. J. Thomson had assumed? That is impossible
—for then the electrons would be drawn into the nucleus by the
electrical forces of attraction. Perhaps, then, the electrons move,
circling the nucleus as planets circle the sun? This vision of the
atom as a minute planetary system is fascinating. Yet there are
objections that cannot be ignored. According to the laws of
electro-dynamics, the circling electrons must continuously emit
light—not like real atoms, which do so only when their radiation
is 'activated': they must continuously lose energy, and they must
inevitably end by falling in towards the nucleus. There is no
clear way of avoiding this catastrophic conclusion.

From the beginning, Niels Bohr is aware that only Planck's
quantum theory offers a way out of this dilemma. The quantum
theory must explain the existence and construction of the atom!
This is Bohr's bold idea—and its realization becomes his
programme.

After a few months in Manchester he has learnt from Rutherford all that he needs for the moment. At home in Copenhagen

he settles down to his calculations; and at last, after many false starts, comes the flash of illumination that brings the solution.

Before a year is out, on 6th March 1913, a letter from Bohr arrives on Rutherford's desk. It contains the manuscript of the first part of a comprehensive theory, which he asks to have published in England. In the July number of the *Philosophical Magazine*, barely two years after Rutherford's pioneering article, Bohr's theory appears.

It is not difficult to build up a theory from more or less wild guesses. A theory worthy of the name, however, must explain phenomena which have been established experimentally, but which still cannot be understood in the framework of accepted laws—and these abound in the case of the atom. One of the most important is this: every atom can emit (and also absorb) only one definite kind of light, light of quite specific frequencies; and this, under spectrum analysis, gives a so-called line spectrum— every light frequency giving one single spectrum line. The line spectra, of which some are simple and some complex, have been known for nearly a century. The lines fall into regular series, and for the simplest spectrum, that of hydrogen, Johann Jakob Balmer discovered as early as 1885 a mysterious regularity and found a formula by which the frequency of each separate line of a series can be exactly calculated. But he did not deduce the formula; he discovered it empirically. Up to this time, no one had understood the formula; all the many attempts to envisage an atom model that would explain it had failed.

And now comes Niels Bohr, whose theory achieves the impossible: in the case of the hydrogen atom it leads back to the Balmer formula. Not only its general form comes out correctly, but even the numerical constant contained in it (the so-called Rydberg constant) can now be calculated from elementary, well-known constants like the charge and mass of the electron, the Planck constant and the speed of light. And the calculation gives the right value!

This is success beyond expectation. Yet the assumptions on which Bohr bases his new atom model are too bold and unusual, too contrary to all accepted ideas of mechanics and electrodynamics for him not to meet with scepticism and rebuttal. Even Rutherford, from whose ideas he sets out, has doubts. He writes to Bohr: 'The mixture of Planck's ideas and those of old mechanical theory make it hard for me to form a physical picture of what it all means.' At the meeting of the British Association in Birmingham, where Bohr's theory is the centre of discussion, the aged Lord Rayleigh, Nobel Prize winner of 1904 and a recognized authority, states: 'I cannot believe that nature behaves thus, and I can scarcely regard the theory as a correct picture of what really happens.'

At the same conference, however, voices are raised in Bohr's favour—for instance, those of such eminent scientists as Poincaré and Jeans. And so the first round ends indecisively.

But, as time passes, work on the construction of the atom proceeds. Bohr himself and others press on with it; above all, the work of Arnold Sommerfeld in Munich, where he creates a whole school of young scientists, paves the way for Bohr's theory, and finally wins it general recognition.

Nonetheless, the basic objections which the sceptics had levelled against Bohr's method remain, though they may be obscured by its triumphal progress and by the successful interpretation and often exact measurement of many properties of the atom. Only many years later, between 1923 and 1927, when de Broglie, Heisenberg and Schrödinger will establish the quantum theory of the atom on a quite new basis, will it be shown that the doubts already expressed were so well founded that Bohr's captivating conception of the atom as a planetary system has to be abandoned.

Something else emerges, too: apart from the fact that these later developments towards 'quantum mechanics' would be unthinkable without Bohr's preparatory work, it becomes apparent that every practical application of Bohr's theory gives a very close approximation to the exact results; that Bohr's atom model, the planetary atom, represents the last stage in the development of atomic physics at which the atom can be envisaged pictorially. Thereafter, in order to approach even more closely to nature, this development must turn away from the representational to the formal and the abstract, which rigorously excludes any pictorial concept of atomic processes.

As yet all this lies in the future; for the moment Bohr's theory (even though it is concerned with the electrons encasing the atom, and is therefore only peripheral to our theme) remains a application of the idea of the nucleus, inconceivable without and standing or falling with its accuracy. It is still disputed but the balance is tipping in its favour. Yet its victory will b that of the nucleus, helping to anchor this firmly in the realit of physics. Thus, then, Niels Bohr is also a pioneer of th nucleus, which is now beginning to assert and maintain its right

But before this stage is reached, the curtain of the First Worl War falls upon the hopeful prelude to a great new developmen

6

ORDER IS HEAVEN'S FIRST LAW

ONLY nine of the substances which we now call chemical elements were known to antiquity: iron, copper, mercury, silver, gold, lead, tin, carbon, and sulphur. By 1500 three others had been added: antimony, arsenic, and bismuth; by 1700 two more; phosphorus and zinc. The eighteenth, and especially the nineteenth, centuries are the classical age of discovery of the elements. When, in 1809, the German chemist Lothar Meyer and simultaneously the Russian Dimitri Mendeleiev set up the periodic system of the elements, they had sixty-three known elements on which to base their initially puzzling tabulation. Had not so many elements already been known at that time, the regularity to which they are subject could never have been discovered. For the Periodic System of the elements is a system for *all* elements, those still unknown as well as those known. And here, in the remaining gaps, lay its great significance for the future—and if the gaps had been too numerous, the discovery of any order would have been as hopeless a task as deciphering a fragmentary text in an unknown language.

Yet Meyer and Mendeleiev could have no notion that, for all the orderliness of their system, they had overlooked a number of gaps, the places of the five elements discovered only between 1894 and 1898 by the English chemist William Ramsay (after Lord Rayleigh had first found argon); these are the inert gases. Ramsay found these strange gases—helium, neon, argon, krypton and xenon—which, unlike other elements, form no chemical compounds, as small admixtures in air. The commonest, argon, accounts for about 1% (strange that it was not discovered sooner), whereas the others are present only in tiny quantities; helium for instance, constitutes a two-thousandth and xenon only on hundred-thousandth of one per cent of a given volume of air.

The discovery and the correct ordering of the inert gases mad the periodic system complete enough for the counting over o the elements, including the gaps, to lead to the correct numbers from number 1 (hydrogen) to number 92 (uranium). The nev system, though its implications may not have been understoo yet, reduced to a well-founded order the confusion once pre vailing in regard to the chemical elements.

Scarcely, however, was this order established, when destruc tion threatened it again: directly upon the discovery of the iner gases followed that of the radio-active elements. In 1898 Mm Curie found polonium and radium, in 1899 Debriene foun actinium, in 1900 Rutherford found thorium emanation an Dorn radium emanation, and in 1902 Giessel found actiniun emanation.

The first radio-active elements fitted easily into the periodi system. Polonium belongs in space 84, radium in the gap at 8 and actinium in the gap at 89. The three newly-discovered iner gases, however, presented their difficulties. All three seemed t belong in the gap at 86. Yet there is no doubt that they are thre quite distinct substances, composed of three different kinds o atoms, which decay at different rates with quite different half lives. Finally, utter confusion was created when new discoverie continued to be made, when the 'X' elements appeared, uranium X, thorium-X, actinium-X—and then their derivatives, all th radio-active decay series began to take shape with their A, B, C C' and C" stages and all that follows, when radiothorium, th two mesothoriums and ionium made their appearance. Withi ten years a good two dozen different radio-elements had come t light. All of them should, on the basis of their atomic weigh and genetic relationship, belong in the periodic system betwee bismuth (no. 83) and uranium (no. 92). But according to Adan Riese there are only eight places between 83 and 92, some o which, moreover, already had their undisputed occupants. The problem, then, seemed insoluble: the abundance of the radio elements threatened to shatter the order of the periodic system

It was also particularly difficult to assign to the new radio-elements definite places within the periodic system. Most of them existed only as traces that cannot be weighed, being recognized solely by their characteristic radiation. In most cases it was impossible to determine their atomic weights. The investigation of their chemical properties is very difficult, and little had yet been achieved. Yet this was the only approach which might offer an explanation. Now the order of the day was —chemistry. For years the physicists had been setting the pace in research—studying radiation, counting the particles emitted, measuring the rate of decay and calculating decay energy. Now the chemistry of the radio-elements must come into its own.

★   ★   ★

The Chemistry of the Radioelements is the title of a book of which the first volume appeared in 1911 (Longmans, Green & Co., London); it throws the first light upon the ordering of the radio-active elements in the periodic system. Its author is Frederick Soddy, a lecturer at Glasgow University.

Soddy is no stranger to us; he it was who, at the age of twenty-three, joined Rutherford in Montreal in 1900, and with him investigated the decay and recovery of thorium-X; the Rutherford-Soddy theory of decay carried his name round the world. He had worked under Sir William Ramsay (the discoverer of the inert gases) in London, and had provided the first experimental proof of the belief that alpha particles consisted of helium. Since 1904 he has been teaching physical and radio-chemistry at Glasgow University, where he has been working on the chemistry of the radio-elements. He is repeatedly struck by groups of substances which appear to be chemically identical and which are distinguishable only by their physical, radio-active properties. Radium emanation, thorium emanation and actinium emanation form one such group. Uranium I (ordinary uranium, the 'father' of uranium-X) and uranium II (a derivative of uranium-X) form another. Similarly the radiothorium discovered by Hahn, the ionium (the 'father' of radium) discovered by Boltwood and common thorium belong together. Another pair of substances (also discovered by Hahn) to which Soddy devotes special attention is mesothorium 1 and radium. In his

famous book Soddy presents in a new light all the knowledg
gathered over the years about the difficult, still fluid scientifi
field of radio-activity.

The chemistry of ionium, for instance—as this book tells us—
can be described in one sentence: its chemical nature exactl
resembles that of thorium, so that no separation of the two ele
ments is possible by any known process, and no concentration o
either the one or the other can be achieved.

Or again: the chemistry of mesothorium 1 can be similarl
described: chemically, it is identical with radium and cannot b
separated from it.

Such sentences occur repeatedly in the book. Thus Sodd
revealed a fact that was decisive for all that followed: there ar
groups of radio-active substances whose chemical properties ar
indistinguishable, and which are therefore chemically the sam
substance, the same single element, although their radio-activ
behaviour may show various differences. He sums up this nev
discovery in general terms in the second volume of his boo
(1913). For such substances as are only differing varieties of on
and the same element, and cannot be separated from each othe
by chemical means (and, indeed, at that time by any other means)
he coins the term which has remained one of the most importan
in nuclear physics: *isotopes*.

*   *   *

Meanwhile a host of scientists has followed Soddy's lead an
turned to the chemistry of the radio-elements. Alexander Smit
Russell and Alexander Fleck are working with Soddy in th
Glasgow laboratory, the Hungarian George von Hevesy is i
Manchester with Rutherford, in Karlsruhe the young Germa
physical chemist Kasimir Fajans is starting his academic career
in Berlin Lise Meitner has recently arrived from Vienna to wor
with Otto Hahn, in Holland there is Antonius Johannes van de
Broek; and at the Cavendish with Sir J. J. Thomson there i
already the man who, born within twenty-four hours of Soddy
though in another county, vastly extends the scope of the isotope
some ten years later: Francis William Aston.

The ceaseless labours of this large, international group o

scientists quickly dispels any remaining uncertainties. The concept of the isotopes becomes progressively stabilized. And this concept resolves at a single blow the apparently insuperable difficulties of fitting the radio-elements into the periodic system. The impossibility of accommodating two dozen elements in eight places immediately vanishes, when it is accepted that several elements may occupy each place. Now, however, one no longer speaks of several *elements* which belong in one place, but of several *isotopes*, which all have the same chemical properties and which all represent the same element, though as different varieties of it, and must therefore occupy the same place in the system.

At the same time, it is possible to distinguish the various isotopes of a single element by their radio-active properties. Thus radium emits alpha radiation and lives 1,600 years (half-life), while its isotope mesothorium 1 emits beta radiation and lives barely 7 years. The three emanations all emit alpha radiation, but have half-lives of 4 days (radium emanation), 1 minute (thorium emanation) and 4 seconds (actinium emanation).

The isotopes of a single element also differ in one other respect: their atomic weight. Radium has the atomic weight 226, but its isotope mesothorium 1 has 228. Both belong at 88 in the system. The three emanations, all belonging at number 86, have atomic weights (in the same order as above) of 222, 220, 219. We may remember that we have already mentioned two different types of uranium with atomic weights of 238 and 235, both at 92 in the system, and also several sorts of lead (number 82) with various atomic weights. These, too, are examples of isotopes. Uranium is also a radio-active substance; lead is not, though all the varieties of lead derive from radio-active decay series.

We can now clearly characterize every isotope by stating to which element it belongs and its atomic weight. Thus we speak of uranium 238 and uranium 235, of lead 206, lead 207 and lead 208; to which are added the radio-active isotopes of lead: radium-D, thorium-B, actinium-B and radium-B, which, in the same sequence, we can call lead 210, lead 211, lead 212 and lead 214. For mesothorium 1 we now write radium 228 ('normal' radium is radium 226), for the emanations of radium, thorium and actinium we now write emanation 222, 220 and 219.

The abundance of the radio-elements is in no way limited by the concept of isotopes; but it is given a new orderliness. All radio-elements are now neatly arranged in the few places between the numbers 81 and 92 (both inclusive), always in groups of isotopes.

Van den Broek set the coping-stone to this order when he perceived that the number of an element in the periodic system, now the common number of all its isotopes, represents nothing more nor less than the number of electrons in the shell of its atom or the charge number of its nucleus.

The nucleus of the atom! The circle closes. The arrangement of the elements and their isotopes depends upon the nucleus, upon this idea so recently propounded by Rutherford. Everything that a few years earlier seemed so confused is now so clear and simple. Isotopes of one element occupy the same number in the system—that is: their atoms have the same number of electrons, and nuclei of like charge but different weight. That these nuclei of different weight show differing radio-active properties is no longer a matter of surprise; for radio-activity is a property of the nucleus. That the various isotopes show the same chemical behaviour is no longer mystifying, for chemical behaviour is a property of the electron shell, which in the isotopes of a single element consists of the same number of electrons and is obviously similarly constructed. But then the various isotopes of an element must emit the same light frequencies and have the same line spectra. And this, too, will soon be proved true.

Once more we have to revise our definition of the atom. The statement that an element consists of atoms that are identical is wrong. Now it must read: a given isotope of an element consists of identical atoms. The element itself may be a mixture of several isotopes, thus containing atoms of various kinds, all of which certainly have identical electron shells, but different (even though similarly charged) nuclei.

The number of different sorts of nuclei, then, is clearly greater than the number of chemical elements—greater than 92. Just how great it is, will only emerge very much later.

*   *   *

The tabulation of the elements, now so firmly established, is further attested in yet another way: by X-rays.

Before publishing his discovery, Röntgen himself had investigated his rays so thoroughly that for many years there was nothing left for other physicists to do. Among other things, he had found that different sorts of X-rays can be produced: rays of greater or lesser penetration, 'harder' or 'softer' rays. The greater the voltage across the discharge tube which produces them, the harder are the rays and the greater their penetration.

This and much else, then, was well known soon after the discovery of the rays. Nevertheless, new problems arose in connection with them. Among the scientists who devoted themselves to their solution, one of the most energetic and successful was the Englishman Charles Glover Barkla, whom we have already mentioned several times, and who now, in 1911, had been working for some years at King's College, London.

Barkla, having already made several important discoveries, had turned to the question of what happens when X-rays strike solid substances. The rays penetrate these substances and are gradually absorbed in the process, thus growing weaker the further they penetrate, and doing so the more quickly the softer they are. This had long been common knowledge—but this is not all. The rays are scattered by the substance upon which they fall. If the rays are directed on to the substance from *one* direction, they are scattered from it in *all* directions. This, too, was common knowledge; but Barkla used it to a new and significant purpose. He succeeded in calculating from the intensity of the scattered radiation the number of electrons composing the electron shell of the atoms of the substance that causes the scattering. And from the results with many elements, he deduced that the number of electrons—at least in the case of relatively light elements—is approximately half the atomic weight. We have already discussed this, and have seen how the establishing of this fact formed a link in the ever-growing chain which finally encompassed the ordering of the elements.

But this was still not all. Barkla also found that the scattered X-rays are not uniform. When he exposed a body, say a lump of copper, to X-rays of a definite penetration, there were among the rays scattered by the copper several kinds of rays of *varying* penetration. *One* part of them always retained the same penetration as that of the rays striking the copper. Other parts were of less penetration, and—what was the remarkable thing about it—this penetration remained constant, no matter if Barkla exposed the copper to rays of varying hardness. Only when he substituted for the copper a small lump of iron or zinc did the penetration of this component of the radiation change.

Now, in September 1911, Barkla had obtained a sufficient number of results to be able to sum up his findings, which appear thus:

All elements (chemical compounds behave according to the amount of the individual elements they contain), when they are exposed to X-rays, not only scatter the radiation to which they are originally exposed, but also emit a new radiation of a different (and smaller) penetration.

The penetration of this new radiation does not depend upon that of the original radiation, but solely upon the kind of element exposed to the latter.

The new radiation consists of two components, one harder (known as K-radiation) and one softer (known as L-radiation). Later other components, M, N . . . radiation are discovered.

The penetration of both the K- and L-radiation increases regularly if one proceeds from element to element according to the increase in atomic weight.

These, then, were Barkla's findings. A sequence of increasing atomic weight? But this—with a few exceptions—is the sequence of the elements in the periodic system! Clearly there is here a new principle, beside that of atomic weight, for arranging the elements in their proper order. And now an interesting question presents itself: to arrive at the correct system, it is—inexplicably!—necessary in a few instances to offend against the principle of arrangement by ascending atomic weight. How would it be if the elements were ordered according to the penetration of their 'characteristic radiation'?

Barkla was ready with the answer to this as well. In the element series cobalt, nickel, copper (i.e. at one of the places where there is an 'irregularity' in the table of atomic weights), he found a *regular* progression in the hardness of the radiation. Hence the 'characteristic radiation' of the elements is not merely another principle of tabulation; it is a better one.

By 1911, however, the basic question as to whether X-rays are corpuscular or wave radiation was not yet decided. Barkla believed it to be the latter; his calculations of the number of electrons in the atom were founded on the assumption that they are wave radiation. But there were still scientists of repute who held them to be corpuscular radiation.

'Corpuscles or waves?'—this had gradually become a burning question, and it was one that had provoked lively discussion at the Institute of Theoretical Physics at Munich University, which had for some years been directed by Arnold Sommerfeld. Here, too, was another versatile theorist: Max von Laue. It occurred to him that, if X-rays are wave radiation, then they must be diffracted by regular structures, just as light is by diffraction gratings or by glass with a series of lines scratched close together on it.

This was no new idea. Since Röntgen's time, repeated—and always unsuccessful—experiments had been made to show diffraction. But Laue suspected that the experiments failed because the wave-length of the X-rays is too small, far smaller than that of light, so that optical diffraction gratings were too clumsy. And they could not be improved upon artificially. But does not nature itself provide more delicate diffraction gratings? Does not the remarkable theory of the French crystallographer Bravais, who had been dead these forty-five years, suggest that all crystals consist of a completely regular, grating-like arrangement of atoms of the most delicate structure? Might not this natural crystal grating diffract the X-rays, might they not give a fine, regular pattern of dots on the photographic plate after passing through a crystal?

This was the thought that struck Laue, and he set to work at once.—Or rather, he did not do the work himself, for he was a pure theorist. He joined with two experimental physicists, Friedrich and Knipping, who carried out the experiment under his guidance.

Strange things happened in this spring of 1912 in the laboratory—a few improvised rooms—of the Sommerfeld Institute. As yet there was no reliable X-ray apparatus. Knipping had therefore constructed an automatic switch for the experiment, which was to extend over several hours, so that the apparatus could alternately be switched on for a few seconds and then off for a few seconds. As the result of some faulty connection, the oscillations of the contact-breaker were picked up by the arc-lamps of the street-lighting in the Amaliestrasse. Passers-by, hearing the queer, repeated sawing noises, whispered: 'Shh! Professor Sommerfeld is snoring!'

After twelve hours of excited waiting, the plate on which the X-rays had fallen, after passing through a copper sulphate crystal, came out of the developer. And the regular pattern of dots was there!

Further experiments with another crystal, with zinc blende and with more exact adjustment of the crystal, gave even better pictures. The experiments dispelled any doubts that X-rays are waves, and that Bravais' grating theory of the construction of crystals is correct. On 8th June 1912 Sommerfeld presented the work of Laue, Friedrich and Knipping to the Bavarian Academy of Science.

The nature of X-rays becomes clear: it is certain that they are wave rays, and their wave-lengths can also be measured by the crystal diffraction method. It transpires that the wave-length provides an exact measure of what has hitherto been called the greater or lesser 'hardness' of the rays. Hard rays have very small, soft ones greater wave-lengths. But always these wave-lengths are from a few thousand to several tens of thousands of times smaller than those of light.

All these new discoveries had their effect on the regularities observed by Barkla. Now that wave-lengths could be measured, it would surely be possible to establish them more accurately. The man who devoted himself most energetically to this task was a young Englishman who had been working for a few years with Rutherford in Manchester: Henry Moseley. Quickly he measured the wave-lengths of the K-radiation of a large number of elements. He found an extremely simple and exact regularity, according to which the wave-length of the K-radiation diminishes as the atomic number of the element increases. 'Moseley's Law' permits the calculation of the atomic number (i.e. the number in the system) of every element whose place may still be in doubt, by measuring experimentally the wave-length of its K-radiation. This guarantees a definitive tabulation of the elements—and a much better one than that by atomic weight, whose regularity is disrupted by exceptions.

There is, however, one disturbing feature in this otherwise orderly regularity. Nearly all the places in the periodic system have a single occupant—the one kind of atom of the particular element. Only in the places at the top, from 81 upwards, which are occupied almost exclusively by radio-active substances, do we find various groups of isotopes clustered in each place. Why do the elements with the highest atomic numbers behave so differently from the rest in this particular?

*   *   *

Meanwhile Sir Joseph John Thomson, Rutherford's former teacher, had been doing some interesting experiments at the Cavendish Laboratory in Cambridge. He was still preoccupied with ions in gases, the positively charged formations which remain when one or more electrons are torn out of the shell of a molecule or an atom. Alpha particles are such ions, though ions of a special kind: namely helium atoms without their two electrons—consisting, then, of the bare nucleus. As we know, it had been possible to measure their charge/mass ratio very accurately by subjecting a stream of alpha particles to deflection through both electrical and magnetic forces.

Thomson now carried out similar experiments with ordinary gas ions, i.e. those from which not all the electrons, but only one or at most two (out of many) had been removed. He deflected streams of such ions electrically and simultaneously magnetically across their path, and so could read the charge/mass ratio from the parabola-shaped black lines traced by their impact on the photographic plates, just as had been done a few years before with alpha particles. As nearly all ions have the same charge— one elementary charge, for doubly charged ones are very rare— the position of the parabola on the plate depends entirely upon the mass of the ions, upon the atomic weight or the molecular weight, according to whether they are ionized single atoms or molecules, and this could be seen on the plate. The picture showed what kind of ions compose the stream.

And now it appeared that there is never only *one* kind of ion. Thomson always found several parabolas on the plate, even when he was experimenting with pure gases. If he fed in, say, carbon monoxide, CO, he got parabolas at the figures 2, 12, 16, 28 and 44. The explanation is that 2 is the molecular weight of the hydrogen molecule H_2, 12 and 16 are the atomic weights of carbon C and oxygen O, 28 (= 12 + 16) is the molecular weight of CO, and 44 (= 12 + 16 + 16) that of CO_2. The hydrogen presumably came from the grease on the glass taps of the discharge tube, which is vaporized by the electrical discharge, the carbon and oxygen atoms from the break-up of the CO, and the CO_2 molecules from the odd O atoms attaching themselves to unconsumed CO molecules.

Thus Thomson, with his 'parabola method'—the simultaneous deflection, both electrically and magnetically, of streams of ions—could make the most exact chemical analyses of mixtures of gases, and also study the chemical changes that take place in the discharge itself.

One day in the late autumn of 1913 Thomson was experimenting with air which had been enriched, by fractional distillation, with the light inert gases helium and neon. Besides the parabolas of oxygen and nitrogen, he got other parabolas at the atomic weights 4 and 20, and a very weak one at 22. Helium has the atomic weight 4, neon 20. But 22? Could this mean that he had discovered yet another gas?

Thomson repeated the experiment with every possible mixture of gases. The line at 22 is always observed when neon is present, that is, whenever line 20 appears. And no matter what other gases are present, it is regularly ten times weaker than line 20. But whenever line 20 does not appear (when there is no neon in the tube), line 22 is also missing.

This allows of only one explanation: the new gas of atomic weight 22 is always formed in association with neon, mixed in the proportion 1:10. Can this mean that this new gas *is* neon, a neon isotope, neon 22 together with 'normal' neon 20? Can it mean that all natural neon consists of these two isotopes mixed in the proportion 1:10, and that it cannot be broken down into its constituents except by this technique of electro-magnetic analysis of the stream of ions?

This would be entirely compatible with Soddy's recently discovered isotopes in the field of radio-active substances. And it
would also substantiate an old prophecy made in 1886 by Sir
William Crookes, now eighty years of age, who suspected that
all elements (nothing then being known of the radio-active ones)
might in fact be a mixture of several sorts of atoms with different
whole-number atomic weights.

This extremely interesting question captured the special
attention of a colleague of J. J. Thomson's, who had helped him
in all these experiments: Francis William Aston. Yet neither he
nor Thomson himself succeeded in making a systematic study
of the problem, for which the prerequisite would be a more
accurate apparatus for controlling the streams of ions. Their
work was cut short by the outbreak of the First World War;
pure research gave place to war work, and a year later all had
changed. Young Moseley had been killed in the Dardanelles,
Aston had gone to the Royal Aircraft Establishment at Farn-
borough. And so neon 22 remained only a pointer for the future,
and the innumerable isotopes of the common, non-radio-active
elements, which will complete the grandiose order, had to wait
another six years before emerging into the light of science.

7

THE NEW ERA

IN spite of four long years of war and disruption, pure scientific research was not completely submerged. Albert Einstein built up his general Theory of Relativity and set it out in definitive form in a work of 1916. Arnold Sommerfeld in Munich developed Bohr's model atom, and between 1915 and 1918 was busy setting down his new and comprehensive conception in his book, *The Construction of the Atom and Spectrum Lines*. In Munich, too, Walther Kossel, in 1915, perfected the idea of the electron shell, correctly explained the origin of K and L X-rays in the atom, and laid the foundation of a theory of chemical combination—of the union of atoms and molecules. In Berlin, James Franck and Gustav Hertz jointly proceeded with the work on the ionization and excitation of atoms by electron bombardment. Robert Andrews Millikan, in Chicago, refined his method of measuring the electrical charge of the electron and could now measure it accurately to within a few thousandths.

The Braggs—the father a Professor at Leeds, the son a lecturer at Cambridge—vastly improved the measurement of the wave-lengths of X-rays (X-ray spectroscopy) as did also the young Swede, Siegbahn, of the University of Lund, where he was beginning to establish a famous school.

In the field of radio-activity, Otto Hahn and Lise Meitner in Berlin discovered protactinium, the missing element at gap no. 91.

Following up work begun before the war, Wolfgang Gaede in Freiburg and Irving Langmuir in the laboratory of the General Electric Company at Schenectady constructed novel vacuum pumps, the mercury vapour or mercury diffusion pumps which made possible a proper vacuum technique, and thus also many later pieces of apparatus used in nuclear physics.

Many others were working quietly away, unaffected by the general turbulence of the war, so that in spite of the difficult working conditions, the lack of trained assistants, and of the international exchange of information, a great deal of important new material was brought to light during these years, and now at last it could be absorbed and evaluated. But all this was over-shadowed by the great sensation—Rutherford split the nucleus!

*   *   *

What does this really mean? First, it means an unpretentious experiment with an unexpected result. Rutherford has been accelerating alpha particles of radium-C through the air. He observes the scintillations they produce when they strike a fluorescent screen. These particles have just sufficient energy to penetrate 7 cm. through normal air—that is to say, they appear only when the screen is moved to within 7 cm. of the radiating substance; at a distance of 7 cm. the scintillations, i.e. the alpha particles, suddenly cease. But not everything ceases; Rutherford observes a very small number of weaker scintillations at greater distances, and these only disappear completely at 40 cm. Particles of greater range (40 cm.) must therefore be present besides the normal alpha particles with a range of 7 cm. This is an unexpected result.

Is this so very startling? It might be thought that radium-C emits another, as yet undiscovered radiation which consists of particles of greater penetration. But this is not the case! Mysteriously enough these penetrating particles appear only in air, or more especially in pure nitrogen, but are absent in pure oxygen. Clearly they are connected in some way with nitrogen and can only arise in this element.

The results of the experiment are simple and unsensational. It is the explanation which is astounding: the penetrating particles prove to be nuclei of hydrogen—H-particles or protons, as we should say nowadays. The protons arise in the nitrogen with which the apparatus is filled, and since no hydrogen is present there, the protons must have split off from the nuclei of nitrogen.

The nitrogen nucleus has been 'split' or, as we should say to-day, transmuted, as a result of the collision with the alpha particle.

This result is fantastic! The nucleus of a light element, a usually completely stable nucleus has been transmuted by artificial means! The thesis of the complete immutability of chemical elements had been dealt a severe blow by the discovery of radio-active substances, the nuclei of which are in a constant state of mutation—but in their case the process cannot be induced or influenced by external interference, and the nuclei in question are somehow abnormal ones, limited to the heavy atoms at the top of the periodic table of elements. Now, however, nitrogen— a 'normal' element—has been transmuted artificially by external interference. Immediately a host of new questions arises.

First, what sort of element is produced when a proton is split off from a nitrogen nucleus and flies away with great force? For some time to come this question remains unanswered.

Second, is nitrogen an exception? Can all the elements be transmuted similarly? Three years later, in 1922, Rutherford discovers that in addition to nitrogen, the nuclei of the elements boron, fluorine, sodium, aluminium and phosphorus release H particles when bombarded with alpha particles. They, too, may be 'split'.

For some four years Rutherford and Chadwick at the Cavendish Laboratory have a complete monopoly in atom-splitting. Then Gerhard Kirsch and Hans Petterson in the Radium Institute in Vienna also start to experiment with the splitting of H particles from atomic nuclei. Soon it is clear that neon, magnesium, silicium, sulphur, chlorine, argon, and potassium can be split. Yet it also becomes apparent that not all nuclei— particularly those of the heavier atoms—can be split by bombarding them with alpha particles.

This may be because the energy of the alpha particles used was insufficient, yet alpha particles with their several million electron-volts are the most powerful 'missiles' available; no one dreams that in a few years it will be possible to produce missiles with an energy of up to several milliard electron-volts, missiles which no nucleus can withstand.

Then arises the question: what happens to the energy produced when an atom is split? Are similar energies liberated as in the natural mutations of radio-active elements? The transmutation is produced by the alpha particle which strikes the nucleus with a certain energy, thus splitting off a proton which flies away with a certain energy. It is eventually shown that in many cases, but not in nitrogen, the proton has far greater energy than the alpha particle which strikes the nucleus. That is to say, energy is produced by the artificial transmutation of an atomic nucleus, energy comparable with that liberated by the mutations of radio-active nuclei. Not all nuclear transmutations produce energy; in many cases (e.g. nitrogen) energy is used up. Soon scientists start to differentiate as in the case of chemical reactions, between exothermic and endothermic transmutations —those that produce energy and those that consume it, the amounts of energy in question being about a million times greater than in the case of chemical reactions.

Thus the artificial transmutation of nuclei opens up the enormous reservoir of nuclear energy. Will the dream of the exploitation of atomic energy, which has proved fruitless in the case of radio-active substances, now be realized? Will the dream of the alchemists now be realized and elements be transmuted? Will gold be made from base metal?

However epoch-making the results may be in the world of science, ideas of practical exploitation remain Utopian—each alpha particle can at most transmute one nucleus. The alpha particles produced by rare and expensive radio-active substances are far too few, even if every one were effective, to transmute any real amount of matter and so liberate much energy. As it is, not every alpha particle which is fired into a gas (or solid substance) causes a transmutation. It is a matter of chance whether the particle will strike a nucleus—on average, only one particle in 20,000 strikes a nucleus and produces the desired effect.

What really happens when an alpha particle strikes a nitrogen nucleus? What sort of a particle is produced? What is the final result? At present it is only known that a particle of hydrogen, a proton, is produced. But what remains of the nitrogen nucleus?

In order to understand how this question was answered, it is necessary to take a look at the experimental aids used by nuclear physicists in the early twenties.

* * *

There were three pieces of apparatus used by the early workers on radio-active radiations: the fluorescent screen, which glowed with a greenish light under the influence of strong radiations; the photographic plate which became black when exposed to radiation, and the ionization chamber in which the rays produced ions whose total charge could be measured by an electrometer.

Since those early days the means of observation and measurement have been increased and considerably improved. Many of them are so sensitive that they register individual atomic particles—alpha particles or electrons travelling in the radiations. In 1908 Erich Regener, at that time in Berlin, showed that the scintillations, the tiny flashes of light which illuminate a fluorescent screen exposed to alpha radiation, are caused by each individual particle producing one flash of light, and thus established a method of counting alpha particles. We have just seen how important this method was in Rutherford's experiments.

In 1908 too, Hans Geiger, Rutherford's assistant in Manchester, invented an electrical device which registers and counts ionised particles—a device finally perfected in 1928 in the form of a counting tube which not only counts alpha particles, but also electrons, and later radiation quanta and neutrons—a device destined to achieve fame under the name 'Geiger counter'.

Only when it was possible to prove the existence of atomic particles, were the last doubts as to their existence finally overcome. The famous Austrian scientist, Ernst Mach, had been a violent opponent of the atomic theory all his life; 'Have you ever seen one?', he used to ask mockingly. Only as a very old and sick man, when he actually saw the scintillations caused by the atomic particles in the 'spinthariscope' could he believe unreservedly in their existence. Even Max Planck, creator of the quantum theory, was always sceptical of his own discovery, and on first hearing the crackling of the radiation quanta in the Geiger counter he is reported to have murmured, 'Well, they do exist after all!'

A still stranger piece of apparatus is destined to come from the Cavendish Laboratory. Since long before the discovery of radioactivity, Charles Thomas Rees Wilson, son of a Scots farmer, has been employed in the Cavendish. After studying zoology, botany, geology, physics, and chemistry he has developed a special interest in meteorology—particularly in the formation of fog and clouds.

As early as 1895, shortly after coming to the Cavendish to work under J. J. Thomson, an article by him appeared in the *Proceedings of the Royal Society* on the condensation of water vapour in air to form drops of fog, when the air, saturated with water vapour, is suddenly cooled by rapid expansion. The condensation of water vapour was to be the great pre-occupation of his whole life. Tirelessly patient, C.T.R., as his colleagues call him, works away with his cloud-chambers. He discovers that the formation of fog is hastened by X-rays and the new radiation of uranium, that the ions produced by these radiations provide condensation nuclei around which the drops of water collect. Even before the turn of the century J. J. Thomson suggests in a letter to Rutherford in Montreal the possibility of using Wilson's cloud-chambers in his experiments, and for a time Rutherford uses the instrument, but to no avail. Radio-active impurities, which he cannot eliminate, militate against any real success, and Rutherford turns his attention to other, more rewarding methods.

But the dour Scot in Cambridge doggedly pursues his own line of research; no test of patience is too great for him, and at last his unequalled patience brings its reward. On 11th May 1911 he is able to deliver a paper to the Royal Society on the uses of his perfected cloud-chamber. High-speed particles passed through it become visible as minute white fog trails. At first it is only possible to photograph the relatively strong traces of the alpha particles and the formation of fog caused by the multitude of tiny traces produced by the secondary electrons liberated by X-rays. Two years later it is possible to register the exact path of both alpha and beta particles in their flight, and gamma and X-rays by the traces of their secondary electrons. A series of fine photographs illustrates Wilson's treatise, which appears in the *Proceedings of the Royal Society*.

That which had previously been considered impossible had been achieved. It was now possible to see individual atomic particles 'in flight'. The white traces seen in the Wilson chamber, as the apparatus is now called, are, of course, not the particles themselves, nor yet the ions they produce in the course of their flight, but they are the tiny drops of water which collect around the ions and thus plot the course of the particle itself, and which may aptly be compared to the vapour trails of aircraft flying at high altitudes.

The Wilson chamber, constantly improved throughout the years, becomes one of the principal aids of the nuclear physicist. Some forty years later another kindred method of registration comes to be widely used. Just as the tracks of ions are marked by condensed drops of water in the saturated water-vapour of the Wilson chamber, so too are they marked in the gelatine of a photographic plate by crystallized grains of silver. The Wilson chamber shows the tracks white on a dark background, the photographic plate black on a white background. Yet a few decades are necessary before the photographic plate, the oldest means of proving the existence of radio-active radiations, can be perfected as the most sensitive instrument for the registration of the paths of atomic particles.

★   ★   ★

Amongst the scientists using Wilson's cloud-chamber as a means of investigating radio-active substances is a certain Patrick Maynard Stuart Blackett, also of the Cavendish Laboratory. This former naval lieutenant, who resigned his commission in order to study physics under Rutherford, succeeds in improving the photographic techniques used with the Wilson chamber. He photographs the tracks of the particles from two directions at right angles to each other, and can thus reconstruct the exact position in space of the tracks.

This technique is now applied to the study of the collisions of alpha particles with other atomic nuclei, and it is shown that the track of the alpha particle suddenly divides, one track being the path of the displaced nucleus and the other being the track of the rebounding alpha particle. His colleagues joke that Blackett is playing billiards with atomic nuclei, and indeed, by means of the hundreds of photographs of the angles which the tracks form, and from the speeds of the particles which he can deduce from the length of the tracks, he can prove exactly the validity of the laws of elastic collision, the very laws which govern the game of billiards.

But Blackett is ambitious; might it not be possible to photograph the splitting of the atom in this way? The main difficulty lies in the extreme rarity of the phenomenon, so that it would be necessary to make thousands of exposures in order to be sure of success. In order to meet this difficulty, Blackett constructs an automatic device which takes a whole series of photographs at regular and frequent intervals of what is happening in the nitrogen-filled chamber. In all, Blackett makes some 23,000 exposures, which show the tracks of some 400,000 alpha particles; and eight of these actually show the nucleus being split. The picture is not unlike that of a normal collision. Here, too, the track of the alpha particle divides at the place where it strikes the nucleus. One of the two branches is long and thin (the track of the penetrating proton), the other is short and thick (that of the transmuted and displaced nucleus of hydrogen). But what has happened to the alpha particle? If it had continued in its flight, its track would certainly be visible; yet no photograph shows a third track. Thus visible proof is found for the earlier hypothesis that the alpha particle remains embedded in the nucleus with which it collides and becomes incorporated in it.

Only now is it perfectly clear what is involved in the 'splitting' of a nucleus—a proton is lost by the nucleus concerned, which in exchange incorporates into itself the alpha particle which collided with it. We should therefore speak of nuclear transmutation, and a simple calculation will tell us the nature of the transmuted nucleus.

The nucleus of nitrogen has 7 elementary charges and 14 units of mass (7th element in table of elements and atomic weight 14), add to this the alpha particle—a nucleus of helium with 2 elementary charges and 4 units of mass—and we have 9 elementary charges and 18 units of mass. Subtract from this a proton with 1 elementary charge and 1 unit of mass. Result: 8 elementary charges and 17 units of mass. The 8th element in the table of elements is oxygen, therefore the nucleus of nitrogen has been transmuted into a nucleus of oxygen.

But, it may be objected, oxygen has the atomic weight 16, not 17. The concept of isotopes which is now gaining general support would, however, explain this difference. Up to now, Aston has only found oxygen with the normal atomic weight 16, but no one doubts that oxygen 17, to which our calculation points, does in fact exist, and a few years later it is indeed discovered as a rare component of the oxygen in the atmosphere.

Wilson's cloud-chamber celebrates a great triumph, and there are others to follow. But this first one is sufficient to bring its creator the Nobel Prize in 1927. Blackett, too, will one day join the ranks of the Nobel Prize winners, but as a result of subsequent work, again with the help of Wilson's magic box.

*   *   *

While these experiments were in progress, a development of great significance for the subsequent progress of nuclear physics was taking place in the very same building. The war over, Francis Aston returned to the Cavendish, where he had previously worked under J. J. Thomson. Before the war, the latter had discovered that there were two different sorts of neon, one with an atomic weight of 20 and one with an atomic weight of 22, and Aston had hoped to test this result with more accurate apparatus and to examine the possibility that other elements, too, might have isotopes. Now, after an interval of six years, he was free to follow this line of enquiry.

The first essential was a more exact and sensitive instrument for the electrical and magnetic deflection of rays of ions, a method used by Thomson to differentiate and separate ions of different weights. But Thomson could only separate ions which differed in weight by at least 10%. Aston succeeded in building a piece of apparatus which separates ions whose difference in weight is only one per thousand. This 'resolution of 1 in 1,000', as the scientists call it, represented a great step forward. The term 'mass-spectrograph' gained currency for these instruments which sort ions according to their mass and record on a photographic plate the mass-spectrum of the gas-content of the apparatus. Even Aston did not suspect how the mass-spectrograph would be developed, and that in two or three decades it would lead to resolutions of 1 in 50,000 or 1 in 100,000, and that it would be possible, by this means, to define the mass of an atom (compared to a normal atom) correct to six decimal places.

Four months after the completion of his mass-spectrograph,

in December 1919, Aston had confirmed Thomson's results with neon and found in addition to neon 20 and 22, evidence of a neon 21—yet a further isotope.

With great enthusiasm Aston started to experiment on other elements. His suspicions were confirmed: of eighteen elements examined, exactly half proved to be mixtures of several isotopes —usually two, but sometimes more. In the case of the inert gas krypton Aston found six isotopes, in xenon five (a further four were later discovered in this latter element).

Almost more remarkable is another result which Aston obtained simultaneously: the atomic weight of all isotopes proves to be expressible in whole numbers. There is no neon with an atomic weight of 20·35 or 21·87. The figures produced by a machine which works correct to a thousandth are exactly 20 and 22, and the same holds good for the other elements examined. Those elements whose atomic weights are not whole numbers prove to be a mixture of isotopes expressible in whole numbers. Thus chlorine, with the atomic weight 35·46, appears in nature as a mixture of definite proportions of chlorine 35 and chlorine 37, the mixture giving the atomic weight 35·46.

Further investigations confirmed these results. By 1925 Aston had examined no less than fifty-six elements, many of which he recognized as mixtures of isotopes, the atomic weight of all pure isotopes being expressible in whole numbers. The single exception to this rule is hydrogen, which does not have the atomic weight 1·000 but 1·008 (oxygen = 16 being the norm to which all atomic weights refer). An atom of hydrogen is thus, when considered from the point of view of this 'law of whole numbers', too heavy by 8/1,000. Can we disregard this?

Let us disregard it for the moment. The beauty of the discovery lies in the fact that the idea of isotopes is no longer restricted to radio-active materials, but includes light as well as heavy elements. It is perhaps a little disturbing that not all elements have isotopes—only a decade later will it be discovered that there is no single element which is not capable of having several isotopes.

The fact that all isotope atoms can be expressed as whole numbers challenges us to the postulation that the nuclei of all atoms are made up of units of equal weight (the shell of electrons is so light as to be of no significance, in view of the accuracy of modern measuring methods). Are these units protons? This seems probable. Scientists recall the old hypothesis of William Prout, a London doctor, who had maintained that all atoms were made up of atoms of hydrogen; only now we must say nuclei rather than atoms. At least we are no longer disturbed by the many elements with fractionally expressed atomic weights which did not fit into Prout's theory, and which we now recognize as mixtures of isotopes.

We are, however, somewhat disturbed by the 8/1,000 too much in the atomic weight of hydrogen, or to express the problem differently, we are disturbed by the deficit of 8/1,000 which all atoms show as against the weight they should have if they were made up of a whole number of protons. As the means of measurement are perfected, it is found that this deficit, this 'mass defect', as it is called technically, is not 8/1,000 in every case, but may be lower or greater by 1 or 2/1,000.

Aston and his contemporaries found a solution in Einstein's formula $E = mc^2$: mass alters as energy alters. Does not the energy of a number of protons change when they unite to form a heavy nucleus? Energy is lost as a result of their union, therefore their weight must decrease too. The slight differences would thus be explained by changes in the energy content. Atomic mass and atomic energy are thus linked together. It was, however, some time before this view with its magnificent confirmation of Einstein's formula and the ideas of the nuclear physicists could be substantiated by concrete scientific proof.

Yet a further problem arises. If the oxygen nucleus, for example, is made up of 16 protons giving an atomic weight of 16, the positive charge of the nucleus should be 16 elementary charges. But oxygen has only 8 elementary charges (no. 8 in the Periodic System). What has happened to the other 8 charges?

Most scientists assumed that another 8 electrons, which have a negative charge, are incorporated in the nucleus and so compensate the 8 surplus positive charges. Others, Rutherford among them, postulated the existence of particles devoid of electrical charge. As early as 1920, Rutherford had considered the possibility of the fusion of a proton and an electron to give an atomic particle with an atomic weight of 1, yet being devoid of electrical charge. If this were possible, the oxygen nucleus could be composed of 8 ordinary protons and 8 that carried no charge. But Rutherford's attempt to find experimental proof for the existence of such particles proved fruitless. William Harkins, an American, invented a name for these hypothetical particles—they are not charged, electrically speaking they are neutral, and so he coined the word neutrons to describe them.

Thus the concept of the particle which will lead to the atomic bomb and the atomic machine was born. Ten years before it actually appeared in nuclear physics, its name was already coined.

8

BREATHING SPACE

FIFTEEN years passed between man's first contact with the phenomena of the nucleus, the radio-active processes, and the discovery of this nucleus itself. A further eight years elapsed before the first artificial transmutation of the nucleus was achieved beside its natural transmutation in radio-active decay. It would seem that the way was open to vast new fields of research, to the transmutations of elements on an unimagined scale.

But the appearance deceives. A hopeful start was made: the transmutation of the nitrogen nucleus by bombarding it with alpha particles was extended to a number of other elements. And there it stopped. The only weapon the scientists possessed, the alpha particle, failed. The majority of elements, and especially the heavy nuclei, resisted every attack. Even the experiments with the few transmutable elements were disappointing, in that the amounts transmuted were so tiny, because of the small number of alpha particles emitted by the radio-active preparations. In fact, experiments could only be made with single atoms, and there could, for instance, be no question of testing the transmutation products by chemical means.

Research had reached a dead end. Missiles of yet greater energy than even the alpha particles of thorium-C' with their 9 million electron-volts were needed—and many more of them were needed. Nature affords neither particles of greater energy, nor more particles of the same energy. It was certainly possible to accelerate ions to high energies in a discharge tube, and also very many more ions (e.g. protons, helium nuclei, and others), than the number emitted by the radio-active preparations, but still to nothing like so great an energy as that of natural alpha particles. The highest potentials produced in the insulation testing fields of the electrical industry were not above a few million volts; and no one had yet ventured to build a discharge tube for even *one* million.

When we look back after the unexampled progress of about 1931 to 1934, it may seem as if, in this decade of deferred hopes, research in nuclear physics was pausing for breath before the great advances to come.

Only the limited field of nuclear physics, however, is resting. In other fields of physics great things are being done—which, though they do not immediately concern us, caused such a radical transformation in physics (and particularly in atomic physics), that the nucleus is drawn into their vortex. Around the middle 1920s the theorists have come into their own; their motto is—abstract mathematical form.

*   *   *

Mathematics is built up on clear, logical relationships more than any other discipline; and to the pure mathematician its application in any other sphere—in the sciences, in technology or daily life—is a profanation of his mode of abstract thought. Nevertheless, it is precisely this application which, over the years, has given mathematics an importance that it would otherwise not have attained. And the science that has most profited from mathematics, in some instances has indeed coalesced with it, is physics. The partial coalescence of mathematics and physics has produced a special kind of scientist: the theoretical physicist.

To calculate from known formulae special instances of physical phenomena is not the business of the theoretical physicist, but of his assistant. The generalization of a formula over a field for which it was not originally conceived is a part of his activity; but his highest achievement is to track down the appropriate, all-embracing mathematical formulation for empirically established facts, and thus to predict the results of experiments not yet performed.

For a long time the mathematical forms in which physical

processes are expressed remained closely allied to mechanical representations, and by illustrating them in plastic terms, made them 'comprehensible'. Only in our twentieth century was it recognized that such illustrations offer at best a one-sided and partial representation of the reality, especially where atoms and molecules are concerned, and that it is possible to find abstract mathematical forms which express more accurately the actual conditions, although they sacrifice their pictorial quality.

It was the cross-fertilization of theoretical and practical physics that led to the burst of progress in physics, and especially in atomic physics, in the twentieth century. But it did not thereby become any simpler, and David Hilbert, the Göttingen mathematician, was not entirely wrong when he said: 'Physics is much too difficult for the physicists.'

*   *   *

One day—sometime early in 1921—a young man who has just finished his schooling comes to Professor Sommerfeld in his Institute in Munich. He wants to study theoretical physics. Sommerfeld says: 'I suppose you mean physics; you can think about specializing later on.' He replies that he has no liking for practical work; he really does mean theoretical physics, and he would like to begin right away with the quantum theory. Even Sommerfeld, who had been a pure mathematician and had never done any practical work himself, is taken aback by such one-sidedness. But something about the young man appeals to him, and so he admits him to his classes in his first term. When he registers for the course, he signs himself Werner Heisenberg.

It is soon evident that Heisenberg is something of a mathematical prodigy. Quite early on he tackles and solves difficult problems. But his chief interest still lies in the quantum theory and the construction of the atom, or more precisely of the electron shell of the atom, the theory of which his teacher Sommerfeld has done so much to advance.

For some years now it has become more and more plain that there must be something wrong in this field of research, that there must be flaws in its very foundations. A mass of semi-empirical regularities has been found, but every effort to interpret them satisfactorily in theory has failed. Theoretical calculations can deal exactly with only one single atom—the simplest, that of hydrogen—with which Niels Bohr had set the ball rolling. Even the next simplest atom, that of helium with two electrons in its shell, proves recalcitrant. Its relatively complex line spectrum defies explanation, and the value given for the binding energy of the electrons by the Bohr-Sommerfeld theory is wrong. Moreover, the theory as a whole is unsatisfactory. To calculate the movement of the electrons in the atom shell the laws of the old, classical mechanics are used, though they are limited by apparently arbitrary 'quantum rules', whose deeper significance is not understood. Obviously a new mechanics must be created—a system for atomic dimensions, differing from classical mechanics and comprehending the quantum theory in its basis. Yet the best brains of the age have not succeeded in finding this mathematical form for the processes of the atom.

Heisenberg is soon absorbed in these ideas. After three years he graduates at Munich, and then goes to Max Born, the theoretical physicist at Göttingen University, where he starts his career as a university teacher, and then also for a while to Niels Bohr in Copenhagen.

On 29th July 1925 an article of Heisenberg's, that makes quite a stir, appears in the *Journal of Physics*. Heisenberg, not yet twenty-four years old, develops in it some remarkable ideas as to the part played by the quantum theory in the mechanics of the electrons in the atom. Although much of it remains tentative, the boldness of the new ideas calls forth general astonishment: all who read the article feel at once that here is the new, long-sought mechanics which governs the processes in the atom.

A few more articles follow, now in collaboration with other Göttingen scientists—Max Born and a young lecturer Pascual Jordan, the son of a well-known painter. Heisenberg's name has become a star of the first magnitude in the physicists' firmament almost overnight.

By the end of 1927, we find him, still not twenty-six years old, as Professor of Theoretical Physics at Leipzig University.

★   ★   ★

Meanwhile this problem of the mechanics of the atom had been attacked from another side. In 1924 a French prince of the old de Broglie family, who had taken up theoretical physics, produced a doctoral thesis in which he formulated some remarkable ideas. Louis de Broglie maintained that the rays of moving corpuscles, for instance cathode rays, beta rays, and alpha rays have the properties of waves—which up to now had been the exclusive right of the wave rays, that is, of light, X-rays, and gamma rays. He deduced this from new connections which he built up between the ideas of Einstein's Theory of Relativity and those of Planck's Quantum Theory.

In their day, de Broglie's notions seemed so capricious that they were scarcely noticed. Only an Austrian, Erwin Schrödinger then a professor at Zürich University, took them up and developed them. And three years later the validity of de Broglie' ideas and of his formula was demonstrated by the famous experiments of the American physicists Davisson and Germer in the laboratory of the Bell Telephone Co.: experiments with electron rays, which showed diffraction by crystals just as X-rays had done, and which thus showed themselves to be waves, whose wave-length can be measured. And this also demonstrated the double nature of the 'corpuscular' rays as corpuscle-waves, which since Einstein's light quanta, had been recognized as a peculiarity of the 'wave' rays.

But before this very important discovery had been reached experimentally, and before the significance of de Broglie's conception had been understood, Schrödinger in Zürich had derived from an inspired extension of it a new mechanics for atomic processes: a system of wave mechanics, which substitutes for the electrons of the atom a kind of continuous wave. Four articles following in rapid succession in the 1926 volume of the *Annals of Physics* set out this system of wave mechanics.

At first it may seem that there were now two systems of mechanics, that of Schrödinger and that of Heisenberg, and that a bitter struggle must flare up between them. Yet Schrödinger himself was able to show that, in spite of their different points of departure and their differing external forms, the two mechanics coincide in all their statements, and are thus two presentations of the same factual content.

And finally the same set of ideas came in still another garb from a third source. Paul Adrien Maurice Dirac, the twenty-three-year-old English mathematician (the new mechanics was indeed a revolution of young minds, with the one exception of Max Born, who was forty-three), worked out in Cambridge at the end of 1925, independently of Heisenberg—Schrödinger in any case came later—his own formulation of the mechanics of atomic processes. Again, it does not diverge substantially from the others. After years of fruitless effort, the challenge of this problem had suddenly, within a short time, been overcome by different scientists, all approaching it from various aspects.

From the fusion of these ideas was born the new quantum mechanics; it is abstract mathematical formalism, unrepresentational to a degree, yet applicable to actual atomic phenomena. It does away with the picture of the electrons as planets circling about their centre, the nucleus, which had been the basis of the Bohr-Sommerfeld theory. This now became a make-shift pictorial device, yielding only approximate results, and only in exceptional cases (e.g. that of the hydrogen atom) strictly valid results. The new mechanics shows that, in atomic dimensions, no visible movement or definite path can be ascribed to the particles—for instance, to the electrons—indeed, that what takes place in the atom is not strictly determined, but is subject to the statistical laws of chance.

In spite of the fact that it ran contrary to all scientific thought up to this time, the new quantum mechanics gained acceptance. It eliminates all irregularities that had so far beset the theory; it solves the problem of the helium atom, and of the chemical combination of two similar atoms—for instance, of two hydrogen atoms to form a hydrogen molecule. It permits the calculation—though the mathematical difficulties are immense—of an electron shell and of molecules of any degree of complexity.

Thus, at the close of the 1920s, just before the breathing space in nuclear physics ended, quantum mechanics and the theory of the atom stood ready, an imposing and close-knit structure, which later required only minor rectifications.

★   ★   ★

All this is concerned primarily with the electron shell of the atom, for which the nucleus provides only the field of force that binds them to itself, and for which only the electrical charge of the nucleus is decisive—and not the possible way in which this nucleus itself may be built up of individual particles.

But quantum mechanics claims to be valid not only for the electron shell, not even only for electrons in any field of forces: it claims validity for *any* kind of atomic particle, and thus also for the particles of which the nucleus consists. Is it now possible to envisage a theory of the construction of the nucleus, to attempt to explain theoretically the phenomena of radio-active decay and of the artificial transmutation of the nucleus?

One thing is very encouraging: quantum mechanics maintain that atomic processes are not strictly determined, but are subject to the laws of chance. Now, one of the best examples from an experimental view-point of a statistical process that is subject to these laws of chance is the radio-active decay of nuclei. It is never possible to state *which* nuclei will decay within the next second—that is a matter of chance; but the statistical laws determine *how many* nuclei will decay within the next second.

A theory of the construction of the nucleus based on quantum mechanics meets with far greater difficulties than the theory of the electron shell. Here only identical particles (electrons) have to be dealt with, and the reciprocal effects of their force is exactly known. But in the nucleus there are at least two sorts of particle—they are mostly assumed to be protons and electrons—and there are grounds for believing that, as far as possible, there are inside the nucleus itself two electrons united with four protons to form close-knit alpha particles; so that there would be three sorts of particles. Moreover, it has long been recognized that the well-known electrical forces cannot be operative between the components of the nucleus—clearly, these forces play a subordinate part in the nucleus—but that a quite new type of 'nuclear forces' operates here, about whose size and properties only vague assumptions can be made.

Yet it was tempting to measure this new weapon of quantum mechanics against the nucleus. And, as occasionally happens, this was done in two places at the same time; in each case the partial solution was the same.

One of the scientists to attack the nucleus theoretically was a young Russian from Odessa, Georg Gamov, who now, in 1928, had just taken his doctorate at Leningrad, and who spent the next two years visiting Göttingen, Copenhagen, and Cambridge. From Göttingen the manuscript containing the theoretical explanation of nuclear decay with the emission of alpha particles was sent off to the *Journal of Physics*.

At this same time two Americans, Gurney and Condon (who came from Alamogordo in New Mexico, near where the first atom bomb was exploded), were working on the problem at Princeton University. They reached the same solution, which they sent to the periodical *Nature*. Unknown to each other, Americans and Russians were competing honourably in 1928 (and less dangerously than twenty years later) in solving the problem of the nucleus; and the Russian just won by a few weeks.

Georg Gamov, who later left Russia and in 1934 obtained a Chair at the George Washington University in the American capital, went further. He offered an acceptable explanation for the artificial transmutation of light nuclei through alpha bombardment, and indicated why it is possible to transmute only the lighter ones. Finally Gamov wrote a book on the construction of the nucleus, in which he helpfully compares this with a tiny drop of liquid. Just as this is made up of closely packed molecules, so also does the nucleus consist of closely packed components, mostly alpha particles, as Gamov assumed, and is not a loose structure like the electron shell.

From this simple model a number of properties of the nucleus could be deduced, at least roughly (and more is not possible in quantum mechanics with a pictorial model). And this could be done although the basis of the whole conception was still very uncertain and the suggested construction of nuclei out of alpha particles, surplus protons, and surplus electrons, was subsequently to be proved wrong.

From this beginning, however, the theory of the nucleus derives; and, in spite of all its difficulties, it will bring many theoretical research workers their triumphs, even though they may not even to-day have completely solved the riddle of the nucleus.

It is noteworthy, too, that this new beginning came at a time

9

THE GREAT ADVANCE

IN the spring of 1927 three Berlin physicists—Arno Brasch, Fritz Lange and Kurt Urban—are clambering about on the steep peaks of the Monte Generoso, round which the lightning of the violent summer storms plays. But they are not climbing for their amusement. The mountain railway brings up steel cables, chains of insulators and screens against flying sparks. A steel chain, 700 metres long and weighing 2 tons, is being stretched from peak to peak.

They are attempting to tap the lightning of the mountain thunder-storms. Since Benjamin Franklin, two hundred years before, had drawn sparks from the tail of his kite during a thunder-storm, it has been known that it is possible to conduct lightning, to derive from it high electrical potentials. Brasch, Lange, and Urban hope to tap many millions of volts from the storms on Monte Generoso—and to use them to split atoms!

They want to wrest from nature what technology has so far failed to yield; to discharge over five million volts across a discharge tube, and so obtain fast-moving particles as atomic missiles instead of the alpha particles, which, though effective, are so few in number. Hence their present activity, and the construction of a discharge tube capable of withstanding several million volts.

Yet their enterprise is ill-starred: by the time various difficulties have been overcome, it is autumn and the summer storms are past. And the following year progress is again slow, although they reach two million volts as the tapped lightning splutters across a striking-distance of five metres. But in August the mountain rebels: Kurt Urban, only twenty-four years old, falls to his death.

Still the others do not give up. They achieve huge arcs—their gauges register eight million volts, and the actual potential may well have been twice as much. The working of the discharge tube, however, presents the real difficulties, and it takes several years to overcome them. In the meantime, other simpler, cheaper, and less dangerous possibilities have been opened up. The advance has by-passed the enterprise of these Berliners.

*   *   *

In 1930 three groups—two in America and one in Britain—have set about replacing the natural alpha particles from the radio-active materials by artificially accelerated 'missiles' of even greater energy, with which, using a greatly multiplied number of particles, to bombard the nuclei. And these need not necessarily be helium ions, that is, 'artificial alpha particles'. A simpler particle, the proton—the nucleus of the hydrogen atom—suggests itself; and later on a third charged missile, also an atomic nucleus, will join them, though in 1930 its existence is still not suspected.

Tuve, Breit, and Hafstad make up one American group, which works at the Carnegie Institute in Washington. They have built a giant Tesla transformer, which is immersed in oil and gives 3 million volts, and under increased pressure, up to 5 million. They have also built a discharge tube capable of withstanding $1\frac{1}{2}$ million volts. By the end of 1931 they have succeeded in accelerating protons at an energy of one million electron-volts. But then they, too, abandon their attempt, because others have by now found a more simple method of producing a stream of high energy particles, which are, moreover, of regular velocity. And so yet another vast undertaking has been superseded.

The second American group is more fortunate. It works in the University of California at Berkeley, half a dozen miles away across the bay from San Francisco. In time they will make Berkeley famous—the Mecca of all the physicists concerned with ion rays of very high energy. The leader of this group is Ernest Orlando Lawrence, a native of South Dakota, who has only recently come to Berkeley from Yale. Among the names of his many collaborators which appear in the group's publications are Livingston, Stanley, Sloan, White, Cooksey, McMillan, and others: here American teamwork records one of its earliest triumphs.

Lawrence exploits an idea recently advanced by a young Norwegian, Rolf Wideröe, who wondered if an atomic particle could not be brought to a high energy by subjecting the same particle to a moderate potential several times in succession. The idea is very sensible—but it is difficult to carry out. A constant potential is ineffective; one that can be altered rapidly is required, and it must be so arranged that the accelerating field can be applied at just the time and place that the particle needs it.

Wideröe had carried out his idea on a small scale. He had tried applying the acceleration twice, and with a potential of 25,000 volts had obtained ion radiation with an energy of 50,000 electron-volts. Lawrence, however, proposes to apply the accelerating field not twice, but a hundred or a thousand times in succession. Surely 1,000 volts would then produce rays of a million volts, and 5,000 volts rays of five million volts!

He tries two methods. He accelerates heavy ions, e.g. mercury ions, in a long straight tube in numerous stages. Soon he attains rays of 90,000 volts with 11,000 volts, and in the next year, with thirty accelerating stages and 42,000 volts, rays with an energy of 1·26 M.e.v.! Here is the beginning of the so-called 'linear accelerators', which will later have such an important part to play.

Lawrence's success with the second method is even more lasting. In the field of a very powerful electro-magnet he bends the ion rays—this time light ones, protons—into a circular path, round which he accelerates them hundreds of times, applying two accelerating fields at appropriate intervals on every circuit. This apparatus is later to become famous as the cyclotron.

With the first trial model, in which the protons run round in a circle of only 10 cm. diameter, Lawrence obtains rays of an energy of 80,000 electron-volts with a potential of 2,000 volts; at the end of 1931, with larger apparatus, he reaches the million electron-volts, and by the end of 1932 the five million. Then he bombards nuclei with his proton rays—and splits them!

But still he is not the first to do it. Others have anticipated him—and with rays of ridiculously little energy—by three months. The English group, thirty-three-year-old John Douglas Cockcroft and twenty-seven-year-old Thomas Finton Walton, has not been idle. They are working in the Cavendish Laboratory in Cambridge, under the direction of Sir Ernest Rutherford, who once again has a hand in the matter.

Cockcroft and Walton, who also started work in 1930, have gone a quite different way. They have studied Gamov's theory of the nucleus carefully, and have concluded from it that—if it is correct—protons ought to penetrate and transmute a nucleus more easily than do alpha particles; energies of only a few hundred thousand electron-volts should suffice.

They do not aspire to produce extremely high potentials, or, at any rate, particles of extremely high kinetic energy. They rely upon what Gamov had prophesied: that protons of moderate energy should achieve their purpose. They are therefore intent upon obtaining potentials of only a few hundred thousand volts, but at the same time a proton ray that is as powerful as possible, that showers upon its objective the greatest number of protons per second.

First, Cockcroft and Walton construct a fairly small pilot apparatus, going up no further than 300,000 volts. In a specially constructed discharge tube they obtain a proton ray which emits as many protons as some two kilogrammes of radium would alpha particles. There are not two kilogrammes of radium in the whole world—it is used by the milligramme—and the alpha particles from radium radiate in all directions, whereas the protons of the Cambridge scientists are concentrated upon a single target. But Cockcroft and Walton do not yet attempt to split the nucleus: 300,000 volts seems to them to be too little. Had they attempted it, they would have been able to record their success as early as 1930. However, they dismantle their apparatus and use their experience to construct a larger one for 800,000 volts. The time lost thus almost costs them the prize of being first. But we must leave them for the moment.

In this year 1930 important events are taking place at the Physical Institute of the Berlin-Charlottenburg Technical High School. There Professor Walter Bothe, a very thorough experimental scientist, is working with Becker on radio-activity. They

are not concerned with high potentials or with artificially produced proton rays of great energy. Bothe and Becker are simply
letting alpha rays from a strong polonium preparation fall on
various light elements—beryllium, boron, and others. It has
been known for over ten years that certain elements are thus
transmuted. But what interests Bothe is rather to find out, by
means of highly sensitive instruments and of Geiger counters
especially adapted to radiation quanta, if any gamma radiation
appears in the process. And, indeed, Bothe and Becker do find
such gamma radiation, particularly strong with beryllium, but
also with boron and various other elements.

A peculiar feature of this gamma radiation of beryllium and
boron, which is emitted only under alpha bombardment, is that
it is hard, harder than any radio-active gamma radiation yet
known, possessing radiation quanta of higher energy than that of
the alpha particles bombarding it. This indicates clearly that
this gamma radiation must be connected with a nuclear transmutation. But why should it appear at its strongest with beryllium, which, according to all experience, cannot really be said to
be transmutable by alpha particles? An insoluble riddle!

At the end of the year, Bothe becomes Professor at Gieszen
University. Becker accompanies him there, and they pursue
their work on this strange beryllium radiation.

This 'artificial nuclear gamma radiation', as Bothe names it,
assumes great significance in nuclear physics, because it affords
a glimpse into the energy structure of nuclei, as a decade earlier
light and X-rays had into the electron shell of atoms. For the
time being, however, its importance lies in a misunderstanding,
which in turn will lead to a wonderful discovery. But before we
deal with this, there is something else to discuss.

Again we go to Princeton University in America. A physicist,
Robert van de Graaff—a native American, though his name may
sound Dutch—has just come here as a Research Fellow, after
extensive studies at the Sorbonne and at Oxford.

At a meeting in September 1931 of the American Physical
Society, van de Graaff reports that he has succeeded in constructing a high potential machine, whose first model had
delivered $1\frac{1}{2}$ million volts, on quite a simple principle. It is a
belt generator. By means of an endless moving belt, rather like

a dredger, an electrical charge is fed into a large insulated metal sphere, until the desired potential is reached.

Van de Graaff's belt generator proves a great success. Soon it can deliver several million volts, later (to save space) it is housed inside a high pressure boiler, and is used in nuclear physics wherever potentials up to about 3 million volts are required, and where this potential must be constant. Above this limit the cyclotron and its later derivatives will hold the field.

In 1930 and 1931 the pace of development has been almost bewildering. On the threshold of the new year, it is true, nuclei have not yet been split by artificially accelerated missiles. Yet two major developments have begun, which will lead to artificial corpuscular rays of an energy never before known. With his cyclotron, Lawrence has produced a potential of $1\frac{1}{4}$ million volts, whose application to rays is soon to follow. The work of Bothe and Becker, of Cockcroft and Walton is proceeding, and has almost reached its goal.

Here the survey of these two years should end; but on the penultimate day of the year, at a conference in New Orleans on 30th December 1931, three American chemists—Urey, Brickwedde, and Murphy—create yet another sensation: they have discovered an isotope of hydrogen, 'heavy' hydrogen with the atomic weight 2.

This is the news that heralds the new year.

*   *   *

The year 1932—the *annus mirabilis* of the physicists—shows the full scope of these landmarks of the advance; the work in progress reaches a conclusion, which again leads to new landmarks.

By 1932 every industrial state has for years been in the grip of an economic crisis; Germany and America in particular are suffering the burden of millions of unemployed. In a tense atmosphere the weak Weimar Republic maintains itself only by emergency decrees in face of the rising flood of National Socialism, which is waiting to seize power. Yet amidst all the political depression of 1932 the seeds of the science of nuclear physics sown over the years come to blossom. So rich is the bloom, that 1932 is the turning-point after which progress broadens out, and from which many, indeed, date nuclear physics as a science.

At the beginning of the year, in the first number of the *Physical Review*, comes the report about heavy hydrogen. Harold Clayton Urey, a chemist at Columbia University in New York, has, with his collaborators, proved the existence of the hydrogen isotope (of atomic weight 2) by its spectrum.

Normally the various isotopes of the same element have the same spectrum. In fact, this is not strictly true: the mass of the nucleus does have a very slight effect on the position of the lines that compose the spectrum. Urey has looked for heavy hydrogen systematically. By fractional distillation he has enriched liquid hydrogen in this hypothetical constituent. He has calculated in advance the spectrum lines that the heavy hydrogen atom should give; and, using his enriched sample, with four thousand times the normal length of exposure, he has actually found them.

On the basis of investigations with the mass-spectrograph of Aston and his successors, hydrogen had so far been reckoned among those elements which have no isotopes beyond the normal atom. But Urey's spectrum method is more sensitive, especially with small amounts, than the mass-spectrograph. And this sensitivity is essential, for it soon appears that heavy hydrogen is present in natural hydrogen (e.g. in sea water) as only one seven-thousandth part.

This highly sensitive method establishes the existence of heavy hydrogen. And a little over a year later heavy water—water whose molecules contain heavy hydrogen atoms instead of normal ones—will be produced by the cubic centimetre, and ten years later by the ton.

Already, however, the significance of heavy hydrogen is great. It is not just another of the isotopes that are discovered from time to time. The nuclei of heavy hydrogen, which soon come to be known as deuterons (and heavy hydrogen itself as deuterium) are new and very simple particles of charge 1 and mass 2, whose simplicity places them half-way between normal hydrogen nuclei (protons: charge 1, mass 1) and helium nuclei (alpha particles: charge 2, mass 4)—particles which are, as it were, half alpha particles. Surely these deuterons, as well as protons and alpha particles, could be used as missiles to transmute nuclei? In less than two years this question will be answered affirmatively.

Yet before any nuclear transmutation by artificially accelerated missiles has been accomplished, still another particle is discovered: one that the physicists have been waiting for, that already has the name neutron. It is the particle which is to give research its greatest stimulus, and which will lead to the ultimate release of the immeasurable energy of the atom.

The confused story of the discovery of the neutron begins in Walter Bothe's laboratory in Charlottenburg. In Gieszen, too, Bothe and Becker have been unable fully to explain the origin of this strange radiation which occurs above all when alpha particles strike beryllium. They find an unusually hard gamma radiation, but they have no idea what kind of nuclear transmutation gives rise to it.

Frédéric Joliot, who has married Irène, Madame Curie's daughter, also begins to experiment with this new radiation in Paris. Frédéric and Irène Joliot-Curie discover something peculiar: if the beryllium radiation falls upon paraffin, a substance rich in hydrogen, protons of great velocity come flying out of it.

Now it might be quite natural for gamma radiation to thrust protons out of the hydrogen atoms in paraffin. But the Joliots calculate that a gamma radiation which produces protons of such high energy should be much harder, ten times harder, than that measured by Bothe. There is a mystery here!

Any discrepancy in experimental physics arouses the suspicion that something quite new lies behind it. Does not the ejection of the protons look as if it were caused by a corpuscular radiation rather than by gamma radiation? Frédéric and Irène Joliot-Curie are on the verge of a portentous discovery.

But they do not make it; the Cavendish Laboratory is quicker. The Joliots published their observations on 18th January 1932. On 17th February an article by James Chadwick describing the discovery of the neutron appears in *Nature*.

Chadwick has been thorough: he has subjected not only paraffin but also many other substances to Bothe's beryllium radiation. In each case he finds nuclei given out—protons with paraffin, nitrogen nuclei with materials rich in nitrogen, and so on. The relationship between the velocities of these various nuclei, however, is incompatible with the assumption that a gamma radiation ejects these nuclei. But they are quite consistent with the assumption that a new type of corpuscular radiation composed of electrically neutral particles of mass 1 is ejecting the nuclei. These particles are neutrons.

Thus not only a new sort of particle is discovered, but also a new kind of nuclear transmutation. Since Rutherford's first success thirteen years before all transmutations had come about through the impact of an alpha particle knocking a proton out of a nucleus, into which the alpha particle is then incorporated. Now, with beryllium, not a proton but a neutron leaves the nucleus. It is soon shown that here, too, an alpha particle is incorporated.

But what about Bothe's gamma radiation? Another fundamental contradiction seems to be developing. Bothe maintains that the beryllium radiation is gamma radiation, Chadwick that it is neutron radiation! Who is right?

Subsequent developments, strange though it seem, prove that both are right. The radiation arising when beryllium is exposed to alpha particles consists of a neutron radiation *and* a gamma radiation, which latter occurs as a phenomenon attendant upon the nuclear transmutation taking place. With his equipment, Bothe could only discover the effects of gamma radiation, while Chadwick's equipment was effective only for the neutrons. And so all the contradictions disappear at once.

The discovery of the neutrons falls like a bomb upon the scientific world. Its effects have not diminished when the next bomb—again 'made in Cambridge'—falls.

Cockcroft and Walton have succeeded in splitting nuclei with artificially accelerated proton rays of moderate energy. In June they are able to report in the *Proceedings of the Royal Society* that they have achieved the transmutation of lithium, boron, fluorine, aluminium, and many other elements. In a number of instances proton rays of 120,000 volts had sufficed to produce a measurable transmutation—though still, of course, of only a few nuclei. So this could have been achieved years before, if only they had risked the attempt.

Three months later Lawrence also transmutes lithium with the proton rays of his cyclotron, and shortly afterwards further elements. This is now the third kind of transmutation we hear of: the missile is the proton. Does it, like the alpha particle, become embedded in the nucleus? What happens there? And what sort of particle is ejected?

All these questions are soon answered. The proton does become incorporated into the nucleus, and what flies out of it is, in this case, an alpha particle. It looks as if the three kinds of transmutation now known are the beginning of a series in which every possible sort of particle is, *mutatis mutandis*, both the missile and the particle split off. And so indeed it is.

Soon the deuteron joins the other missiles; and it proves particularly effective, considerably more so than the proton and much more so than the alpha particle.

And then comes the neutron as a missile. This can be produced only by a nuclear process—e.g. the transmutation of beryllium nuclei by alpha particles—and, since it has no electrical charge, it cannot be accelerated in a discharge tube; yet it is much more effective than all the other missile particles. It can transmute nuclei even when it has quite small kinetic energy, as, being without charge, it is not repelled by the positively charged nucleus, which it can therefore easily penetrate.

At a single blow the foundations of a new branch of science are laid: nuclear transmutations on the widest scale, nuclear chemistry, as it is now often called by analogy with the kindred chemical changes. Twelve years after Rutherford's discovery the various possible nuclear transmutations could be counted on the fingers. In a few years from this time it will be 100, then 500, 1,000 and then 2,000. The nucleus of the atom has become merely the object of man's experimental ingenuity.

*   *   *

The year 1932 is not yet past, nor is its abundance of discoveries exhausted.

Robert Andrews Millikan, the American who nearly twenty years back had devised a method for measuring exactly the electrical charge of an electron, had some ten years before moved from Chicago to Pasadena near Los Angeles as President of the Technical High School of California. So once again California becomes the scene of great events.

For a number of years Millikan has been interested in cosmic rays, which strike the earth from space, and of which we shall say more later. Fast-moving charged particles are in these rays, and they can be investigated with an ionization chamber, a counting tube, or—best of all—a Wilson cloud-chamber, where they leave visible tracks like alpha or beta particles.

Millikan, now over sixty, commissions his assistant Carl David Anderson to build a large Wilson chamber with a powerful electro-magnet, and thus to follow the tracks of the cosmic particles as they are bent by the field of the magnet.

Anderson starts early in 1932. He has to take a great many photographs, as these particles are sparsely distributed, so that a track seldom appears on a plate. A thousand pictures yield only thirty-four tracks, the next 3,000 only sixty-two. Among these are tracks of both electrons and protons—they are easily recognizable. Protons give strong, uninterrupted tracks, electrons fine dotted ones that look rather like a string of pearls. Moreover, the positive protons are deflected in one direction and the negative electrons in the other by the magnetic field.

When sorting over his plates one summer day, Anderson can hardly believe his eyes: is not this electron track curving the wrong way, in the direction towards which the protons, the positive particles, are deflected? Yet the track is undeniably that of an electron. Feverishly Anderson continues his search, and finds among the thousands of pictures fifteen of this electron path that turns puzzlingly in the wrong direction.

In September his first report appears in *Science*, where he says: the particle tracing this peculiar path must be a positive electron!

The report is received by some with sceptical remarks about Anderson's fairy-tales. But the better informed do not sneer. The positive electron, the positron as it is quickly named, does not come as such a surprise to them. For Dirac, the Englishman who had contributed so much to quantum mechanics, had four years before propounded a remarkable theory which had been regarded as something of an oddity, according to which the negative electron must have its positive counterpart, a particle of the same very small mass as the electron, but with a positive instead of a negative charge. And now here is this hypothetical particle of Dirac's, the positron!

At first the positron is a strange guest on our earth. It is no more than a constituent of a radiation coming out of the vastness of space. Soon, however, Anderson has more to report—and other scientists confirm it: positrons are also produced on the earth when the very hard gamma rays of thorium-C" fall on a lead plate. A little later comes the strangest discovery: using a Wilson chamber with a lead plate as the point of origin of positrons in the picture section, one quite frequently sees *two* tracks diverging from *one* point on the lead plate—two electron tracks, one of which bends to the right and the other to the left in a powerful magnetic field. Here, clearly, a positron and a normal negative electron have originated from *one* point. Anderson is not the only one to find such pictures. The Englishman Blackett—already known for his fine Wilson photographs of nuclear transmutations—and the Italian Occhialini, as well as the Joliot-Curies in Paris, and later on many others, all obtain pictures of this sort of 'pairs', of 'twin electrons'.

It is not long before this phenomenon is explained—and one of the most astonishing facts that nature has ever revealed to us comes to light: the two twin electrons are not split off from an atom, a nucleus, or even from any piece of matter, but they are *created* in the moment at which they become visible. They are newly created from the energy of the impact of the gamma quantum, which disappears in the process.

Behind this phenomenon looms once more Einstein's formula $E = mc^2$. But not this time as in the case of the mass defect of heavy nuclei, where a very small change in the mass of already existing particles occurs as the result of an expenditure of energy; no, this time *new* matter, even if it is only an electron and a positron, arises out of the energy of a non-material radiation.

Naturally enough, the physicists now seek the opposite process, the destruction of matter, its dissolution into non-material radiation. And this, too, is found: a positron, coming into proximity with a negative electron, unites with it so violently that both bodies are destroyed and disappear, leaving nothing but a radiation quantum, which has acquired the energy that was previously contained in the inert mass of the electron and the positron.

Thus we can see why the positron is so rare among the elementary particles. It can be created only from the exceptionally

high energy of the hardest gamma quanta, and it is hardly born—
usually in less than a millionth of a second—when it meets a
negative electron, of which there are multitudes, and is destroyed
in immediate fusion, becoming again radiation, from which it
originated. The cycle of cosmic events in the microcosm of the
atom!

All this knowledge of nature's deepest workings results
directly from the discovery of the positron. This alone would
have been contribution enough to future development from this
particle, but it is yet to achieve new and revolutionary significance in another direction.

Neither electrons nor positrons prove effective in nuclear
transmutation, so it is not in this direction. Certainly electrons
of very high energy have a great part to play indirectly, as they
can be used to produce radiation quanta of extreme penetration,
a kind of X-rays, which are much harder than even the gamma
rays of the radio-active materials; and these radiation quanta will
be useful in many kinds of nuclear transmutations. But here
there is not much to be gained directly from the electron or the
positron.

The importance of the positron lies elsewhere. Soon enough
we shall see where.

⋆   ⋆   ⋆

In 1933 the endless processions of the S.A. marched through
the Brandenburg Gate. But as yet few suspected how soon they
would become columns of soldiers marching to a catastrophic
war. From this year, however, we look back on some four years
of unprecedented scientific progress: the walls blocking the
advance of nuclear physics, which had seemed impregnable,
had been breached in half a dozen places. And this had been
accomplished largely by young men, who had succeeded at their
first major scientific attempt: Chadwick was forty-one years old,
Bothe and Urey were thirty-eight, Cockcroft thirty-five, van de
Graaff thirty, Lawrence and Walton twenty-nine, and Carl
David Anderson only twenty-six. These men, most of them at
some time Nobel prizewinners, passed through the breaches they
had made to further scientific victories.

Many of the old guard of atomic scientists, to whom the

nucleus was unknown, were dead: Pierre Curie, Becquerel, Moseley, Ramsay, Crookes, Elster, Geitel, and also Röntgen, whose penetrating rays gave the initial stimulus to the discovery of radio-activity. Madame Curie, worn out by a life of hard work and already in the shadow of death, was still alive, and so was Frederick Soddy, who was to live to an advanced age; and Ernest—now Lord—Rutherford still enjoyed his old vigour, little suspecting that only a few years remained to him.

These pioneers regarded with pride the younger generation which carried on their work. Yet there had been a change: the early work on radio-activity had been done in France and England, and also in Germany and Austria. Now more than half of those laying the foundations of nuclear science were Americans.

And what these men had achieved! New machines produced extremely high potentials, ions raced across discharge tubes to bombard and transmute nuclei. Protons whirled through the magnetic fields of the cyclotron, until they crashed with inconceivable force into their target. In a host of transmutations the nuclei retreated before new apparatus. Heavy hydrogen had been found and heavy water produced, the deuteron was competing as a projectile with the other particles. The long awaited neutron had been discovered and was beginning to play a part of immense future importance. And the construction of the nucleus was no longer a mystery: its components were seen to be not protons and electrons, but protons and neutrons—a fact enlarged on by Werner Heisenberg and the two Russians Tamm and Ivanenko. The theory of the construction of the nucleus now had firm foundations on which to spring up. And then the positron, an elementary particle whose existence had been forecast theoretically, was discovered. The pairs of electrons came to light. The creation and destruction of matter touched upon the basic processes of nature.

Such was the abundance of new material that the four years 1930 to 1933 brought to nuclear physics. And yet the most remarkable discovery, intimately bound up with it all, had still to be made. All was ready, more than ready, for it.

Let us see how it came about.

10

RADIO-ACTIVITY LEADS THE WAY

IN Madame Curie's Radium Institute in Paris there is intense activity. Though tired and ill, she herself attends daily and keeps abreast of each new development. Most active are Irène, her daughter, and Irène's husband, Frédéric Joliot, a man of immense vitality and ability. It is almost as if the good old days in the laboratory have been recaptured: the shining instruments hold promise of great discoveries to come.

Only the year before Frédéric and Irène Joliot-Curie failed by a hair's breadth to make such a discovery when they found the protons which Bothe's beryllium radiation knocks out of paraffin, but did not draw the conclusion (or prove experimentally) that only a new kind of corpuscular radiation could have this effect. Joliot said later that the right idea would certainly have occurred to him if he had read Rutherford's second Bakerian Lecture, where he prophetically envisages the neutron—and then *he* would have discovered the neutron instead of Chadwick. But the Joliots are not the people to mourn long over a lost opportunity; and soon their interest is focused on the positron, which Anderson has just discovered.

The Joliots do not work with cosmic rays, but simply produce the positrons by means of a hard gamma radiation. They investigate the conditions under which positrons arise, and their destruction on penetrating matter or on fusion with negative electrons. They make every conceivable experiment—and in June 1933 they come upon something quite new: positrons arise when they subject the element aluminium, and then also boron, to *alpha* radiation.

Thus a third way of producing positrons is found! But what

can it mean? The elements aluminium and boron are among those whose nuclei Rutherford had already succeeded in transmuting by alpha bombardment: this thrusts a proton out of the nucleus. Yet now, with the same projectile, the Joliots find positrons. That looks just as if a neutron plus a positron is occasionally emitted instead of the proton—which ultimately comes to the same thing, as the neutron has the mass of the proton (and no charge), while the positron has its charge (and infinitesimal mass).

These positrons from a nuclear transmutation, appearing singly and not paired with negative electrons, are of the greatest interest; and the Joliot-Curies are very anxious to throw some light on their mysteries.

And suddenly they make a breath-taking discovery, of which they had never dreamed: aluminium foil which, under alpha bombardment, emits positrons, continues to emit particles for up to half an hour after the alpha radiation is cut off, as a Geiger counter shows. This independent radiation gradually ceases— and does so according to the time law so familiar from the radioactive materials. A half-life can be determined: 14 minutes (later, more exact measurements give some 10 minutes). It is a miracle, but it is clear beyond doubt: the aluminium itself has become radio-active through the alpha radiation! The Wilson pictures show that the particles emitted after the alpha bombardment has ceased are still positrons. Similar results are obtained with the elements boron and magnesium, only here the half-life of the induced radio-activity is shorter.

On 15th January 1934 the Joliot-Curies' sensational discovery is announced to the Paris Academy. 'Artificial radioactivity' is born! It falls to the daughter of the woman whose labours thirty years earlier had brought to light radium and thus rendered possible research into radio-activity, to make this discovery.

The Joliot-Curies are not content merely to establish that aluminium, boron, and magnesium have become radio-active through alpha radiation. They wonder just what is taking place inside the aluminium nucleus. They believe that a nucleus is being transmuted, as in the case of Rutherford's alpha transmutations. Here, too, the alpha particles must surely remain in the aluminium nucleus. This time, clearly, not a proton but a neutron is thrown out by the impact of the alpha particle. Its complementary positron at first remains: the nucleus newly created by the ejection of the neutron has become radio-active and does not release the positron until a little later.

But what is this radio-active nucleus? Not aluminium, as this has already been transmuted. Now some elementary arithmetic is useful: the aluminium nucleus has a charge of 13 and a mass of 27. An alpha particle of charge 2 and mass 4 is added, giving a total charge of 15 and mass 31. From this is taken a neutron of charge 0 and mass 1, leaving a charge of 15 and a mass of 30. According to the table, charge 15 indicates the element phosphorus. Therefore it is a radio-active isotope of phosphorus of atomic weight 30 (whereas normal, non-radio-active phosphorus is 31).

Hence radio-active phosphorus arises from the alpha bombardment of aluminium. But can this well-founded assumption be proved?

Rutherford had maintained that oxygen arises from the bombardment of nitrogen with alpha particles—but the amount of oxygen is always so tiny that it could never be traced by chemical or spectroscopic methods.

In the present case chemical methods would be equally ineffective in tracing the phosphorus—but now it is radio-active! The positron radiation at once betrays the smallest trace. Hence it must be possible to identify the chemical nature of this phosphorus. Similarly the chemical nature of the radio-active nitrogen which simple arithmetic shows as deriving from boron, and the radio-active silicon from magnesium must be identifiable.

In only three weeks Frédéric Joliot and his wife complete this research programme. It is the first time in the history of nuclear physics that a transmutation product can be directly identified chemically. And incidentally it finally proves that the alpha particle remains embedded in the nucleus.

In the following year, 1935, the Joliot-Curies receive the Nobel Prize for Chemistry, which Irène's mother had won twenty-four years before (her second Nobel Prize!) for isolating radium. This great pioneer of radio-activity, however, cannot attend the Stockholm ceremony. On 4th July 1934 she had died of leukemia caused by the radium.

Twenty years later Irène will suffer the same fate.

★   ★   ★

In their first publication of January 1934 the Joliot-Curies had surmised that alpha bombardment was not the only means of inducing artificial radio-activity, but that other particles could be used to produce nuclear transmutations which would give rise to radio-active isotopes.

Physicists all over the world now set to work to develop this new territory: the number of publications describing new nuclear processes and newly discovered radio-active isotopes shoots up. Often the same nuclear reaction is reported simultaneously from different places; and so many are engaged in nuclear physics that it is no longer possible to name them individually.

Not only alpha particles, but also protons, deuterons, and above all neutrons reveal themselves as effective projectiles for making artificially radio-active materials. And these materials, of which over a hundred are soon known, do not by any means behave like the radio-active nitrogen, phosphorus, and silicon of the Joliot-Curies. Not all emit positrons. Soon isotopes are found that emit electrons, like many naturally radio-active substances. Many artificially radio-active materials emit gamma radiation as well as their corpuscular radiation. Later a few are discovered which emit alpha particles and even neutrons.

Radio-active isotopes with every imaginable half-life are found. Most of them are more powerfully radio-active than radium—often a million times more—and only their minute quantity at first prevents their competing seriously with this already outmoded basic material.

There are, for instance, two kinds of radio-active carbon—one of atomic weight 11, emitting positrons, and one of atomic weight 14, emitting normal beta rays (ordinary carbon is carbon 12). Carbon 11 arises when protons and deuterons fall on boron, and has a half-life of 20 minutes. Carbon 14, whose function in determining archaeological age we have described, arises when neutrons strike nitrogen nuclei and has a half-life of nearly 6,000 years. There is a sodium 24 with a half-life of 15 hours, which is produced by neutron or deuteron bombardment of ordinary sodium 23; there is a radio-active phosphorus besides the one obtained by the Joliots, a phosphorus 32 (half-life 14 days), produced by bombarding ordinary phosphorus with deuterons or sulphur with neutrons.

There is a radio-active calcium with a half-life of 6 months, a radio-active iron with 6 weeks, a radio-active iodine with 8 days, and a radio-active gold with barely 3 days.

We could continue this list for pages: soon at least one, and generally several, radio-active isotopes are known for each element. In a few years the number of known isotopes leaps from around 300 to over twice that number. From its preserve among the heaviest elements, radio-activity has extended over *every* element.

Every single element has at least *one* radio-active isotope— even hydrogen, the lightest element. Urey, the discoverer of 'heavy hydrogen', hydrogen 2, had sought in vain for a yet heavier isotope, a hydrogen of atomic weight 3, in natural hydrogen. Now this hydrogen 3 can be produced (even if, like all the other radio-active isotopes, as yet only in infinitesimal amounts) by bombarding hydrogen 2, deuterium, with deuterons, or lithium with neutrons. It is named tritium. It decays with a half-life of about 12 years, emitting a soft beta radiation, and becomes a helium isotope of atomic weight 3. Later it will play an important and terrible part.

Are these newly created materials, these innumerable radio-active isotopes, of any practical significance, or are they of only scientific interest?

*   *   *

Shortly after the First World War Georg von Hevesy, a physical chemist at the Vienna Radium Institute, had interested himself in the rapidity with which ions, of which crystals are made up, change their position and roam about within the crystal. These ions are not firmly anchored for all time, and even though the movement of atoms in solids is extremely slow, after a sufficient number of years there is not one which will still be in the place it started from.

But how can ions be labelled and their movements traced? This is what Hevesy undertook to do. The crystal he used was lead chloride, and he labelled the ions whose movements he proposed to study by using a radio-active isotope of lead. Even then, these isotopes were known to occur in the natural radio-active decay series, and some could actually be isolated in weighable amounts. These radio-active lead ions indicated their position by their radiation, and could easily be distinguished from their identical, but non-radio-active, sisters. And so Hevesy had soon established the rate of movement of ions in lead chloride.

This 'indicator method' of Hevesy's had been used occasionally for a few years past: the 'labelled' atoms indicate the way taken by any substance in any process, however complex. A limiting factor was the small number of radio-active isotopes then known—a few of lead and of bismuth, and that was about all. So only a small range of problems could be attacked by the indicator method.

But in 1934, 1935, 1936 all this had changed. There was an ever-growing multitude of radio-active isotopes—there was a choice: radio-active isotopes could be found for all the elements, though they could not be produced in weighable amounts. It did not matter. However minute the amount, they could be mixed with the basic element, and their radiation would always identify them!

After twenty years, the indicator method bore its full fruit: there were labelled atoms of carbon, of sulphur, iron, gold—of whatever was wanted. The radio-active isotopes, resulting from delicate laboratory experiments, suddenly became expensive commercial products. Most of them are, weight for weight, a thousand or a million times more valuable than gold. Their production in tiny amounts (no one has ever obtained so much as a milligramme) with van de Graaff generators and cyclotrons is difficult and costly. And yet they serve their purpose.

But what is their purpose? Wherever it is desired to follow the course of any substance in any process, however complex, the radiation from the added radio-actively labelled atoms of an isotope will make it both possible and certain. Thus many scientific and technological problems, which formerly could not be attacked, can be solved.

We find chemists analysing complex chemical reactions with radio-active isotopes, following the exchange of ions in various phases, checking the yield of new processes. We find metallurgists using them to study smelting, to discover how much of a valuable metal remains in the dross or how the heating gases work. We find engineers using them to check the efficiency of lubricants, the points (untraceable by other means) at which a machine wears, localizing leaks in pressurized containers or pipes; agriculturists learning from them the effects of their fertilizers, following the path of the phosphorus in their phosphates and of the nitrogen in nitrogenous fertilizers—learning how much of them is absorbed into the plant and how much the fruit benefits.

We see, too, biologists solving with radio-active isotopes long disputed problems of metabolism, following the course of nutrients or poisons in living organisms—in plants and animals, and finally in man. And with this we stand before the gates of medicine: will not a marvellous instrument like the radio-active isotopes revolutionize the art of healing and open up new possibilities in the fight against death?

Here they have their widest application. But we must pause a little, as the question is too large to consider merely from the point of view of the radio-active isotopes. Long before these were artificially produced, the mysteries of radio-activity had brought new aids to medicine—and also new dangers.

Let us, then, return from the stage we have reached, from the turbulent years preceding the Second World War, to the bottom rungs of this unending ladder.

11

THE FIGHT AGAINST DEATH

WHEN Wilhelm Conrad Röntgen, in his laboratory in Würzburg, on the night of 8th November 1895, caught sight of the bones of his hand as a dark shadow in the greenish light of the fluorescent screen, he discovered not only X-rays, but at the same time also a practical medical application for them.

A few months after Röntgen's first publication, the doctors began their own experiments. A Professor Kocher in Bern found the location of a needle embedded in a patient's hand by means of X-ray; a Professor Miller in Cleveland took pictures of a fractured arm; the Emperor William II had his withered arm X-rayed. A Berlin doctor suggested filling the stomach with a less penetrable liquid and thus extending X-ray photography from the bone-structure to the stomach. The idea was realized by the Munich specialist Rieder a few years later with his 'Rieder meal' of bismuth.

The ability to see on an X-ray picture metal objects which have found their way into the body, fractures, and abnormal conditions of the stomach offered a potent new aid to diagnostics. A new technique of diagnosis by X-ray began to develop, though it had a long way to go before it could detect the slightest shadow on the lungs or the smallest abnormality in the heart, as it does to-day.

But something further was also developing. Very early it became clear that X-rays cause physiological changes in living tissue: they cause inflammation of the skin, erythema, burning and X-ray sores that heal very slowly, if at all. Could not such changes in the tissues be controlled and used to combat disease?

The doctor's task is not only to diagnose, but also to cure; nd so now X-ray therapy allied itself to X-ray diagnosis. The kin was first to be treated; as early as 1896 Leopold Freund in ienna had used X-rays for depilation. All kinds of skin and hair iseases were treated with X-rays—with varying success.

Edison, the famous American inventor, took up X-ray therapy nd produced X-ray tubes. American doctors, too, experimented ith the rays. In 1902 Nicholas Senn in Chicago showed that in ertain leukemias X-rays could modify beneficially the com-osition of the blood; and so he established the so-called depth herapy, the treatment of internal organs with X-rays.

Soon X-rays joined the struggle against other diseases— gainst tubercular bones and joints and muscular disorders. nd eventually—about 1910—against the greatest scourge of umanity, cancer. Here there were good prospects for radio-herapy with cancer of the womb. Krönig in Freiburg, Bumm n Berlin, Döderlein in Munich all achieved considerable uccess. Lasting cures were reported in increasing numbers— ut unhappily by no means in every case.

Meanwhile a serious challenge was being offered to radio-herapy. In a single year the radio-active rays had taken their lace beside X-rays. Becquerel's discovery remained fruitless, he uranium radiation being far too weak to be used medically. 3ut then came the Curies with their radium that is two million imes more powerful. And then the radium derivatives, especi-lly the emanation.

None of these could be used in diagnosis. Therapeutically, owever, it might be possible to substitute gamma rays for X-ays, thereby becoming independent of the X-ray equipment nd the high potential necessary for it; thus, as Becquerel put it, ne would have in the radium capsule a waistcoat-pocket X-ray ube. Finally, might not alpha and beta rays usefully supplement he gamma rays, particularly for treating the skin or just beneath t?

So radio-therapy (often called Curie therapy) grew up quite arly on beside the X-ray therapy. From 1900 Dr. Danlos in 'aris was treating tuberculosis of the skin and cancer of the skin vith radium. Among the many pioneers of radio-therapy who ollowed him were Louis Wickham in France, Schücking in

Germany, Finzi in England, and Abbe and Kelly in America
Fifteen years after the great discoveries the battle of the ray
against cancer was taking two paths: in the fight against death
radium stands beside the X-rays.

*   *   *

Yet these new aids had a secret malignity of their own. Still
unpredictable at this time, they turned upon doctor and patient
alike. Not only was their success varied—in some cases they
effected astonishing cures, in others they achieved nothing—but
they also created their own additional dangers.

Soon there were reports of serious X-ray burns; and it was
sinister that these did not show at once. Weeks after exposure to
radiation, mild but increasingly serious symptoms began to
develop: festering wounds, horrible ulcers which defied treatment
and healed only very slowly—if at all. The same applied to radium.
Becquerel and Pierre Curie had felt its malice; Madame Curie's
fingers had long been cracked and rough, unprotected for years
against the attack of the powerful preparations. And she did not
suspect that as yet imperceptible damage had been done to her
whole body, and that it would eventually kill her. A colleague of
Edison's had to have an arm amputated after a single year of
experimenting with X-rays.

The unsuspecting patients, too, were in great danger. Experience in handling this instrument, shrouded still in obscurity
was lacking; it was not yet possible even to measure accurately
the radiation dosage; there were no Vienna or Paris radium
standards. The gravest hazards were still regarded all too
lightly. And so burns caused by overdoses of radiation were
commonplace—sometimes even resulting from straightforward
radiography. Many patients were lucky to escape with their
lives: not from the illness, but from the cure.

Another distressing fact came to light. In 1903 Albers-
Schönberg in Hamburg discovered that rabbits are made sterile
by X-rays; so also are humans. And exposure to very weak
radiation, which has no other visible effect, is sufficient to do it
if sustained over a long enough period. How many nurses engaged in radiography and exposed daily to small amounts of
radiation were condemned to childlessness in these early years of

his ill-understood new technique? How many future troubles
originated here, without the sufferers ever being aware of it?

And another alarming fact: continued exposure to weak
radiation (though considerably stronger than that which causes
sterility) leads after five, ten, or fifteen years to cancer! Radiation
cancer! Ten years after Röntgen's discovery, the first X-ray
worker to die of X-ray cancer was struck down. The cases
multiplied. In 1911 the X-ray specialist Paul Krause counted
fifty-four cases of radiation cancer in France, England, Germany,
and America.

This immediately explained the mysterious cancer mortality
rate among the miners of Joachimsthal, where the radium-
bearing uranium ore was mined. Now these people began to
understand why their average expectation of life was seventeen
years less than that of the other inhabitants of the place.

Radium cancer! The bitter irony, that the very weapon which
man had turned against cancer should itself cause cancer!

Does not the nucleus show itself thus in its true colours: as a
fiend surrounded by its malign and deadly radiance?

*   *   *

But man is not so easily put off in his fight against death. How
many triumphs have the microbiologists won, what blessings has
the surgeon's knife brought! And so now X-ray and radium
therapy must be divested of their dangers.

An unknown danger is always the greatest menace: some kind
of protection is usually possible against the known. Progress
therefore depended on a better understanding of the effects of the
rays, and on a more exact measuring of the dosage. Here the
physicists must help the doctors—every improvement in radio-
metry means better radio-therapy.

It had gradually become clear that quite small doses of
radiation have only a stimulating effect. They were generally
administered as spa or inhalation cures, in which natural radium
waters, containing tiny quantities of emanations from the radio-
active materials in the earth or sometimes of dissolved radium
compounds, play an important part. 'Radium spas' became
fashionable: Joachimsthal in Bohemia, Bad Brambach in the
Vogtland, Oberschlema in the Ore Mountains. Even the

established spas advertised the radium content of their water.

Such as it were homoeopathic radiation cures are quite innocuous, and, indeed, give relief in cases of neuralgia, asthma and other conditions. But such light weapons are naturally useless against cancer; here only treatment with strong radiation doses can promise any success: with X-rays or gamma rays, or for superficial swellings, perhaps even beta or alpha radiation.

Powerful radiation always destroys the tissues that it passes through. It ionizes a large number of atoms, and this sets up complicated chemical and biological processes, which culminate after weeks—hence the peculiar period of latency—in the destruction of the tissues. With cancer, the radiation is intended to destroy: to kill off the morbidly proliferating cancer cells, which otherwise destroy the whole organism. At the same time, it must do as little damage as possible to the surrounding healthy tissue. This is the aim of the experienced radio-therapy specialist and it is only feasible because of the relatively greater susceptibility of the cancer cells to radiation. And it is upon this aim that radio-therapy concentrated.

The original centre of radio-therapy was France, the birthplace of radium. In Paris in 1906 Louis Wickham had founded an Institute for research into the therapeutic effects of radium. Here great progress in the medical applications of radium was made by Dr. Dominici, 'a bundle of energy and enthusiasm', as well-known American radiologist called him—at once chemist, physicist, and pathologist. For even if the more cheaply produced mesothorium discovered by Otto Hahn was being used clinically, radium and its emanation still remained the most important substances for medicine.

It was now in great demand. A tenth of a gramme (100 milligrammes) is not much for a clinic, and many clinics were wanting to introduce radio-therapy. Hence a new radium industry had sprung up, again in France. An enterprising industrialist named Armet de Lisle started the first factory (with Madame Curie as consultant) in Nogent-sur-Marne. As his famous adviser had once done, he too obtained his raw material, the uranium ore, from Joachimsthal.

Before long other uranium deposits were discovered and their radium exploited. Huge amounts of high quality ore lie in the

Belgian Congo, and in the state of Colorado in America. The first uranium rush began, like the Californian gold rush. Uranium became the object of speculation; fortunes were made and lost with the fluctuations of its price. And these conditions had changed but little when an adventurous Canadian, Gilbert La Bine, discovered the vast uranium deposit—prospecting by aeroplane by now—on Great Bear Lake in Canada's most northerly and inhospitable region. And conditions were much the same later still, when a city rose on the site of a new strike, Uranium City, which gratefully erected in its market square a memorial to Gilbert La Bine—in uranium ore!

To start with, however, the element was costly and scarce. The Royal University Clinic for Women, directed by Professor Döderlein in Munich, used radio-therapy in some 700 cases of cancer between 1912 and 1916; but it had only 150 milligrammes of mesothorium. Some American clinics were better off, possessing one or even several grammes of radium, since an indigenous American radium production started in about 1913 from Colorado ore.

The means were still slender. And yet experience accumulated; growing confidence replaced the tentativeness of the early years. Man had learnt to control this new instrument.

It was recognized that radium is no miraculous panacea where cancer is concerned; but the value of this new radio-therapy was also recognized. In certain cases it can be extremely effective. For instance, in the years following the First World War it came to rival surgery as a treatment for cancer of the uterus, and without greater risk, as the operation claimed its victims too.

A stage in radio-therapy had been reached from which only slow progress was possible. Surprises, either pleasant or unpleasant, seemed to be ruled out. Radio-therapy was assured of its place beside the other accepted methods of medicine.

*   *   *

Had the hazards of the radiating nucleus, then, been overcome?

No! In the large field of routine applications, certainly, they had been: patients were now safe from devastating overdoses. And, as long as the carefully computed maximum dose was not exceeded and the safety regulations were observed, the doctors and their assistants were no longer threatened.

But no sooner is some fresh advance made than the hazards are there again in their full force.

Radium had meanwhile found other uses. It had been realized that the property of these radio-active rays of making fluorescent materials luminous could be turned to account in the manufacture of luminous paints. Such paints no longer depended upon being put in the sun to absorb rays that they slowly give out again: they now had their own source of energy in the tiny admixture of radium, which goes on continually emitting its pale green light for thousands of years. Above all, they could be used in the making of luminous dials for clocks.

In the 1920s the Luminous Watch Factory in Orange, New Jersey, U.S.A., went into production. The luminous paint consisted of zinc sulphide with one ten-thousandth part of a radium compound added. In the factory hundreds of girls painted busily away at the watch-faces. There could surely be no danger in that, as the radium was so incredibly dilute! It was easy to calculate that the total radiation to which the girls were exposed was far below the maximum dosage.

How strange, then, when more and more girls complained of headaches and lassitude. And then illnesses began: inflammation of the gums, pyorrhoea, teeth falling out. Many girls had to go to hospital; the matter was investigated, and the cause found to be—radium!

To keep a fine point on their little brushes, the girls had been moistening them repeatedly with their lips, and so continually introducing traces of radium into their bodies. And it does not pass out of the body, but accumulates there day in, day out over the years. Unnoticed, it did its work of destruction, until at length the symptoms appeared. By then, no treatment could help the unfortunate girls. The radium was in their bodies, for ever giving out its radiation.

The seven girls who had absorbed most radium could not be saved; they died after terrible suffering. The survivors brought an action against the firm, but without success—for as yet there was no legal provision for damage attributable to radiation! Such is the story of those girls in New Jersey. It shows how mistaken it was to assume that the dangers had been overcome. At every turn of the way the demon nucleus lurks, waiting to claim new victims.

★   ★   ★

By the time artificial radio-activity made its appearance in 1934, radio-therapy was firmly established. Text-books had been written about it, and it had evolved its own terminology with expressions like radium capsule, radium gun, cross-fire, radium needle, and contact radiation.

And now the situation was suddenly transformed. In place of the few naturally radio-active materials there were hundreds of artificial isotopes with the most varied properties.

New means of diagnosis were offered by the use of labelled isotopes to trace the path of food, of the blood, of medicaments and poisons in the human body; the way in which certain elements gather in many abscesses could be followed with radio-active isotopes.

Now that radium, its emanation, and mesothorium could be replaced by many artificially produced materials, which are capable of giving a more powerful gamma radiation, new medical possibilities arose. And there are also many radio-active isotopes that can be taken by mouth or injected, and are thus able to do their work inside the body itself. Bold visions were conjured up: would not cheaper and more effective artificially produced materials soon be supplanting the costly radium? What about caesium 137, fifty times more powerful than radium—or cobalt 60, three hundred times more powerful!

Instead of the rough and ready ray treatment from outside the body, where much healthy tissue has to be penetrated to reach the seat of the disease, would it not be feasible to introduce the radiating material into the body itself—not by means of a needle, but, broken down into atoms, into the very tissue? Would this be too dangerous? Surely nowadays materials of short and exactly-known life could be selected, so that they do not go on radiating indefinitely like radium, but disappear painlessly after doing their work!

Only one major difficulty stood in the way of the realization of these visions: the production of these marvellous new substances is intricate, lengthy, and costly, and yields only minute quantities. For the radio-active isotopes can be obtained only by nuclear transmutations, for which neutrons are generally used as projectiles—and these must also arise from a nuclear transmutation, brought about perhaps by deuteron rays from the cyclotron.

The very small amounts that could be thus obtained were enough for scientific research, and soon for medical diagnosis as well, but they hardly sufficed for therapy, which requires much more powerful radiation. The yield of the nuclear processes was so terribly small. The artificial radio-active preparations obtained did not correspond to as much as a fraction of a gramme of radium! A source of neutrons still more powerful than the cyclotrons can offer was needed.

Hence, a few years after the discovery of artificial radioactivity, all its potential medical applications remained an aspiration rather than a reality. And before they could become reality peaceful research was disrupted by the outbreak of war; but war was to create, more or less as a by-product of the quest for the atomic bomb, the precondition for a new burgeoning of radiotherapy: the mass-production of artificial radio-active isotopes in the atomic reactor.

* * *

New methods brought new hazards. And again scientists and doctors were faced with the unknown, whose secrets can be bought only with sacrifices. The losses from past decades, moreover, had not yet ceased. Not for years did fate turn the page on the sins committed in careless ignorance. Thus after a long sickness the Viennese radiologist, Professor Guido Holzknecht, died in 1931; even the piecemeal amputation of his arm, eaten away by X-rays, could not save him. And in 1934 Marie Curie herself died.

Now the painful losses, which were the price of the first penetration into the realm of radiation, had taught greater circumspection. How many more victims would nonetheless be claimed, before the foundations of experience in the safe application of this new knowledge were laid?

In the old Hanseatic city of Hamburg, in the grounds of St.

George's General Hospital, stands a simple monument inscribed with names. Among them are Madame Curie, Guido Holzknecht, Heinrich Albers-Schönberg, Friedrich Giesel, Henri Dominici, and many, many others. There are two hundred names: those of scientists, doctors, and nurses of all nations who perished by radiation.

As yet there were *only* two hundred of these victims of the atomic nucleus. For as yet the atomic age had not dawned!

12

MESSENGERS FROM SPACE

RADIO-THERAPY, as we saw, exploits the natural radio-activity of certain springs. In the waters of these 'radium springs' is dissolved chiefly the gas radium emanation, just as acidulous springs contain carbonic acid gas—though in much smaller concentration. But where does this radium emanation come from?

Radium emanation derives from radium; radium derives, by stages, from uranium. And uranium is really not such a rare element. There is more uranium in the earth than silver or mercury, and almost as much as tin or lead. What makes it hard to obtain is the fact that it is very scattered and infrequently concentrated in actual uranium ores. In its diluted form, how-ever, it is more or less everywhere. The strong radium springs rise, it is true, in regions where high-grade uranium ores occur, as in the Ore Mountains. Yet, since traces of uranium are present everywhere, all the earth and the water on it contain traces of radium, and everywhere tiny amounts of radium emanation are given off by the earth, to mix with the lowest layers of the atmosphere. And so we live exposed to continual radiation—although it is extremely weak and quite harmless: for man has lived in it for untold millenniums.

The investigation of these minute traces of radio-active materials in earth, air, and water, and of this barely perceptible radiation is not really the task of the physicist, but of the geo-physicist, who studies natural conditions on the earth and in the atmosphere that have not been modified by man. And only a few years after the discovery of radio-activity the geophysicists had set about this difficult task; and the emanation measurements with highly sensitive electrometers, whose loss of charge shows the tiny current in an ionization chamber (the classical method of measuring radiation), had soon thrown some light on the matter. But not one of these scientists would have dreamed that the study of the earth's natural radio-activity would lead to one of the most remarkable of scientific discoveries.

*   *   *

It is a dull day, this 7th August 1912. The balloon *Böhmen* hovers thirteen thousand feet above the Spreewald. Since it ascended four hours before in Aussig on the Elbe, it has been sailing northwards. The earth is only occasionally visible through layers of cumulus cloud beneath it, while above there is a thin screen of cloud, through which the sun glows dully.

In its gondola are three men. Captain Hoffory, the leader, is the navigator. Now, at 10 o'clock in the morning, he releases ballast to take the balloon higher. The meteorological observer, Wolf, is studying the details of a depression approaching from the west. The third, Hess, a geophysicist from Vienna, who is observing atmospheric electricity, has eyes only for three microscopes, each of which is mounted on a strange tin cylinder, and for his stop-watch. With them he is measuring how quickly the fine threads of three electrometers coincide, as they indicate the loss of charge, which represents a tiny ionization current in the tin cylinders—the ionization chambers. He is measuring the natural radio-activity.

Hess is very excited. He is on the track of a ticklish problem; and this ascent, his ninth, but the first to carry him much above six thousand feet, must be decisive.

The radiation on the ground had already been thoroughly measured. It contains a strongly penetrating component, clearly a hard gamma radiation. Then people had begun to wonder what happens to this radiation in the higher regions accessible to a balloon. Obviously it must diminish, as the emanation given off by the earth, which decays by a half inside four days, would gradually disappear.

Another scientist, Albert Gockel of Freiburg in Switzerland, had made several balloon ascents of six thousand feet and over, and had measured the radiation. To his surprise, it did *not* decrease, but remained fairly constant up to the heights he reached. How could this be?

Now Viktor Franz Hess had taken up the problem. On many ascents he had checked Gockel's findings—and they were right! But so far he had not been much higher than six thousand feet. How would it be above this?

To-day's ascent would bring the answer. Conditions favoured a high flight; but Hess is oblivious to everything except his instruments. And, when ten thousand feet are passed there is a definite *increase* in the radiation! Hess has a strange suspicion in his mind. But now he must not think—he must keep measuring!

The balloon has reached sixteen thousand feet. Hess is still measuring, occasionally making hasty calculations on a scrap of paper. Here the radiation is more than twice as strong as on the ground! This effect cannot possibly be produced by the earth. Now Hess's suspicion becomes certainty.

Six weeks later, on 20th September, Viktor Franz Hess is addressing the 84th Annual Meeting of the Association of German Scientists and Doctors at Münster in Westphalia. He has given a careful account of his measurements. The results are tabulated in figures: the radiation increases with the height. He sums up his conclusions thus: 'The results of these observations seem to be most easily explained by the assumption that radiation of very great penetration enters our atmosphere from above.'

> From above—that is: from space.
> Such is the discovery of cosmic rays.

*　　　*　　　*

It is seventeen years later. Anglers and yachtsmen often see in this summer of 1929 a queer grey motor-boat in an unfrequented part of Lake Constance, half way between the German and Swiss shores. The curious might read the name *Undula* (i.e. Little Wave) on her stern. And, whatever the weather, the *Undula* is at this spot—the deepest point of the lake—almost daily. The minster of Ulm could be set down on the bottom of the lake, and no ship need fear grazing its pinnacle. Beneath the boat lie 800 feet of water.

A peculiar bridge-like construction projects from her stern.

A winch clatters and a steel cable rises foot by foot from the depths. Then a word of command, and the winch turns more slowly. A man with a trim beard, his collar turned up and his yachting cap at an angle, steps out on to the iron platform and looks into the water. And suddenly a yard-wide, black neck emerges, and then a round body three yards across. Another word, and the winch stops; and in the stern of the boat lies not a sea-monster, but an ungainly iron tank. The man with the peaked cap has now secured the monster's neck with wire rope. He begins to loosen the screws of the cover. What is in the tank? Who is this man?

Though he may look it now, he is no professional seaman. He is Professor Erich Regener of the Technical High School in Stuttgart: the same man who made his name twenty years before in Berlin with the first scintillation-counting of alpha particles. And in the tank are super-sensitive instruments which, with the aid of clockwork, have for hours been measuring the intensity of the cosmic radiation at the bottom of Lake Constance.

Cosmic rays at the bottom of the lake? Have they not so far always been sought by balloon in the high, thin layers of the atmosphere? Why, the name 'cosmic ray' is only four years old; earlier they were called 'penetrative high-altitude radiation', as it was not yet certain whether this radiation originated in space or in the highest layers of our atmosphere. High-altitude radiation! Hess had been up to a height of three miles and had found the radiation twice as strong. Then Werner Kolhörster had ascended to over five and a half miles and had found the intensity of radiation ten times greater there. In Texas, soon after the war, Robert Andrews Millikan (famed for determining the electrical elementary charge of electrons to an accuracy of one in a thousand) had reached a height of nearly ten miles, though not in person—the first stratosphere ascent in a free balloon will be made in a few years' time by Piccard; instead, he sent up automatic instruments with pilot balloons. Millikan, in fact, had obtained very divergent results. He had found such a small increase in the radiation with the greater height, that he had doubted the reality of the whole phenomenon—in 1924!—and only later, when these measurements were shown to be unreliable did he again come to believe in cosmic rays and to devote further research to them. All these had gone upwards, and now Regener is probing the depths.

Strictly he is not the first to do it. Millikan himself, his strongest rival at this time in the field of cosmic rays, had already carried out under-water experiments, reaching a depth of 230 feet in a Californian lake. He wanted to know how quickly the residue of the radiation that permeates the atmosphere is completely absorbed in water. His own and others' experiments had shown that cosmic radiation is much more complicated than was at first imagined, and that it is a complex mixture of various rays of differing penetration.

Regener had thought: the deeper I sink my apparatus in the water, the purer will be the component of greatest penetration, as the less penetrating components will be absorbed at smaller depths. And so in the previous year he had already set about getting to the bottom of Lake Constance, at first with such primitive equipment as a rowing-boat stabilized with empty petrol cans. Now, in the summer of 1929, he repeats his experiments on a larger scale and with better equipment. His preliminary results are fully confirmed:

At a depth of 500-800 feet he finds the most penetrating traces of the cosmic radiation in all its purity. It is so penetrating that it must pass through nearly 160 feet of water before its strength is reduced by half. Hence it is one hundred and fifty times as penetrating as the hardest gamma radiation yet known!

No one can credit a corpuscle with such power of penetrating matter. Regener, and many other scientists working on cosmic rays, therefore take it to be a kind of ultra-hard gamma radiation, an extremely short-wave radiation. Hence the name of Regener's boat *Undula*—Little Wave.

Although known for seventeen years to resourceful researchers, cosmic radiation has so far betrayed very few of its secrets. Even Regener's basic assumption is wrong: this hardest component of cosmic radiation is not wave radiation; it is a purely corpuscular radiation. But neither Regener nor the rest can know this, for by 1929 the particle known as the meson is still unknown—this elementary particle with such unexpected properties, that creates radiation of such prodigious penetration, passing through the atmosphere and then hundreds of feet of water or rock.

*   *   *

Three years later, in the summer of 1932—so full of political tensions, but also of astounding scientific achievements— balloons start to rise again. They are sent from Dallas in Texas by Millikan and his colleague Bowen, who have long forgotten the unfortunate experiments of 1922; and from Stuttgart by Regener, who is extending his researches from deep water to the stratosphere. Both use the same two-and-a-half metre rubber balloons (later cellophane proves much better). Both send up light automatic instruments, mechanical marvels. Their methods differ a little: Regener uses a 'team' of two balloons, Millikan a single balloon with a parachute. The balloons reach a height of 14, $15\frac{1}{2}$, 17 miles. They come down hundreds of miles from where they were released, and most are found by farmers in their fields; the scientists then retrieve their apparatus and their scientific prizes—photographic plates with markings incomprehensible to the layman. The apparatus is seldom lost.

The results of Regener's and Millikan's first stratosphere ascents, now repeated year after year, more or less coincide. Gradually a graph of the intensity of cosmic radiation from sea-level up to about 19 miles crystallizes. But the curve has an unexpected appearance!

At first the radiation certainly increases with the height. Yet above about $9\frac{1}{2}$ miles the rate of increase slows down, and above about $12\frac{1}{2}$ the measurements—no longer very precise—indicate almost a decrease in the intensity of the radiation. Can it be that cosmic rays do not originate in space? Is there, at a height of some 12 or 13 miles, a mysterious stratum which emits the radiation, so that it is most intense here?

The scientists might well have despaired, had not the extra-terrestrial origin of the rays been otherwise demonstrated a few years before. A Dutchman named Clay on a voyage from Amsterdam to Batavia had regularly measured the cosmic radiation, and had found a dependence upon geographical—or, more accurately, magnetic, latitude: on the distance from the 'magnetic equator' (which does not exactly coincide with the geographical equator). Towards the equator the radiation grows weaker. Numerous tests by aeroplane at a height of about $4\frac{1}{2}$ miles, undertaken on Millikan's initiative, and extending from the polar regions of northern Canada, over the U.S.A., Mexico, Central America, and across the equator to Peru had confirmed this. But this means that cosmic rays are drawn towards the poles by the earth's magnetic field, which reaches out into space far beyond the last traces of the atmosphere—just as the rays of the sun create the northern lights. These rays do not come from the sun (only later was it discovered that a small proportion in fact does so), but if the earth's magnetic field has so obvious an effect on them, then they cannot come from the atmosphere, and they must come from *outside* it. And further: these primary rays, coming from outside the earth, *must* consist of charged corpuscles, for only these are deflected by a magnetic field.

The peculiar height distribution found by Regener and Millikan permits of only one conclusion—that the bulk of the radiation here is no longer the primary radiation coming from outside, but is a confusing mixture of secondary radiation arising out of the primary in the atmosphere itself, clearly at this height of about 12 miles. This basic assumption will later be fully confirmed.

Opinion as to the nature of this primary and of the various components of the secondary radiation is still divided. In these years 1932 and 1933 it tends in this direction: the primary radiation probably consists of positive and negative electrons (the positive electron just having been discovered by Anderson in cosmic rays!), the softer components of the secondary radiation of electrons or protons, perhaps also wave-rays, and the hardest components (those shown by Regener to occur at the bottom of Lake Constance) probably being wave-rays of the ultra-hard gamma type.

It will soon appear that nearly all these ideas are wrong.

*   *   *

For twenty years now attempts to solve the riddles of cosmic rays had gone on, and they had had but little success. Even so, research in the last ten years had reached an intensity seldom devoted to a single subject. Cosmic radiation had been observed not only in laboratories, but also at the bottom of lakes, in the depths of mines, on ice-clad peaks of the Alps and of the Peruvian Andes. In balloons and in aeroplanes the apparatus for measuring it had been sent up to the greatest heights. Scientists had travelled the world to discover its distribution. Yet the vital questions remained: where does the primary radiation originate, and what does it consist of? What processes take place high up in the atmosphere? What sorts of secondary radiation are produced, and what happens to them on their way to earth and into the earth?

So far the study of cosmic rays had been carried out almost entirely with the ionization chamber. Two new pieces of apparatus brought further progress: the counting-tube and the Wilson chamber.

The counting-tube had been invented only quite recently, in 1928, by Geiger and Müller. It made possible the individual recording of every kind of charged corpuscle that penetrates its walls. Then a method introduced by Bothe and Kolhörster proved particularly valuable in cosmic ray research: the coincidence method. This provides a special switch that releases a counting impulse only when *two* counting-tubes are struck by a particle simultaneously (more correctly, with an interval of less than one ten-millionth of a second).

By the coincidence method, which can be extended to more than two counting-tubes, many puzzles could be solved. At least it showed definitely that a considerable part of the secondary radiation found almost solely on the ground and at medium heights, is corpuscular.

The success of the Wilson chamber method was perhaps even greater. It had been in use for some time, but now it was applied to cosmic ray research on a large scale. The reason is this: since cosmic ray particles are thinly scattered, hundreds of exposures can be made with a Wilson chamber without getting a picture of a single one. But now this can be rectified: a counting-tube is placed at the front of the chamber and another at the back, and the counting impulse of the two tubes with coincidence switching automatically operates the chamber.

It was a tremendous success. First of all, by applying a

powerful magnetic field, the energy of the individual cosmic ray particles could be exactly determined from the curve traced by their path. Though it was already clear from the great penetration of the particles that they must have very high energy, the true values were startling: most of the particles measured have a kinetic energy of from 1,000 to 10,000 million electron-volts! At about this time Lawrence produced particles of *one* million electron-volts with his cyclotron. But long before, twenty years later, such enormous energies as those of the cosmic ray particles could be artificially produced, it had become evident that some particles occur in this radiation, though they are rare, with millions of times greater energy even than this.

Then came the second success, the great surprise—the positron. It was in cosmic rays that Anderson, by means of Wilson pictures, came upon this strange new elementary particle. Thence it made its way into nuclear physics: gamma radiation positrons, nuclear transmutation positrons, artificial radioactivity electron-positron pairs.

The third success came six years later, again achieved by Anderson in Pasadena (now in collaboration with Neddermeyer), and again with the help of a Wilson chamber. Certain persistent discrepancies had aroused the suspicions of Anderson and Neddermeyer, and in the spring of 1938, using a Wilson chamber controlled by counting-tubes, they found traces of a particle with most unusual properties. It had a positive charge, but was neither a positron nor a proton—indeed, its mass was some 200 times greater than that of an electron (the mass of the positron is the same as the mass of the electron, that of the proton 1,836 times greater). The new particle proved to be of extraordinarily high penetration, and also extremely unstable; it decayed spontaneously a few millionths of a second after coming into existence.

Thus Anderson and Neddermeyer discovered the meson, and this called forth a host of new puzzles. At that time it was called *the* meson. To-day we should say *a* meson, or properly: the Mu-meson (which, moreover, occurs in positive and negative varieties), for we now know over a dozen different kinds of such unstable particles, which are comprehended under the general heading of mesons.

Not only the experimental, but also the theoretical physicists were stimulated by the meson of Anderson and Neddermeyer. For three years earlier the Japanese Hideki Yukawa had predicted from theory that there must be particles some 200 or 300 times heavier than an electron—which seemed absurd at the time. These particles, he said, must provide the force which binds together the constituents of the nucleus, the protons and neutrons. Now such a particle had been found! Once more experience seemed to confirm in retrospect a bold speculation!

Doubts, however, soon arose. There appeared to be so little reciprocal effect between the newly-discovered meson and atomic nuclei, that it could scarcely be held responsible for providing the nuclear forces. The rejoicings were premature. Not until ten years later would a meson be found, the Pi-meson, that fits Yukawa's ideas better. In any case, the secret of the nuclear forces has not been completely fathomed even to-day.

Nevertheless, the discovery of the Mu-meson solved another riddle of the cosmic rays: this highly penetrative particle has all the properties necessary to explain the penetrative components of the rays. The few thousandth parts of the radiation that Regener had been able to trace at the bottom of Lake Constance, and which can be found even in mine shafts more than half a mile deep, are likewise corpuscular radiation: they are mesons.

*   *   *

And so now, in 1938, considerable light had been thrown on many puzzles that were still unsolved in 1932. It was now known that the hard component of the secondary cosmic radiation is meson radiation; that the softer secondary parts, which are largely re-absorbed into the atmosphere where they originate, consist of a complicated reciprocal series of electron-positron pairs and gamma quanta—that is, wave radiation, the so-called cascades. And there was good reason to see in the primary cosmic rays which descend from space, but of which practically nothing penetrates down to the earth, a radiation of very high energy protons. This assumption, too, was subsequently to be proved substantially correct, and in ten years it would be possible to send instruments up to a height not only of

19 miles, but with rockets to 60, 90, 125 miles, and to establish the existence of the *pure* primary radiation at about 30 miles above.

But what has this story of the discovery and study of cosmic rays, starting so simply and growing so complex, to do with the nucleus and its science?

The answer is: the origin of the primary cosmic radiation is still largely obscure. Yet the interesting processes caused in the high layers of the atmosphere through the reciprocal action of the primary protons and oxygen and nitrogen nuclei, which lead to the formation of the complicated mixture of secondary radiation, have been extensively studied and have thrown much light on the properties and reactions of the atomic nucleus. As, in the main, energies are being dealt with which at this time could not be approached in the laboratory (and even to-day they have not quite been reached), the cosmic rays may be regarded as a vast high-energy laboratory, given to us by nature. With their aid, nuclear physics has been advanced by the solving of problems which would otherwise have remained hopeless.

The history of the study of cosmic rays, however fascinating it may be, is still but a sub-plot in the drama of the nucleus, which we have followed up to the year 1938. And now we must see how, in this same year, the main action of the drama, the technical problem of the transmutation of elements and of the release of atomic energy, has reached its climax: great events are impending.

To get to the root of these events, we must go back—for the last time—to an earlier date: to the year 1911. Our gaze turns to Berlin.

13

THE DEMON BREAKS LOOSE

IN 1911 the Kaiser Wilhelm Society for the Advancement of the Sciences was founded under the inspiration of Adolf von Harnack; on 23rd October 1912, in Dahlem in the western part of Berlin, two of its institutes, designed for pure research, were opened by the Kaiser himself: the Institute for Chemistry and the Institute for Physical and Electrical Chemistry. A Kaiser Wilhelm Institute for Physics was later built nearby in 1936.

The director of the KWI for Physical Chemistry was Fritz Haber, the discoverer of ammonia synthesis (the Haber-Bosch process) and later a Nobel prizewinner; the director of the KWI for Chemistry was Ernst Beckmann. The name of Otto Hahn was among the members of the Institute from the beginning, and soon afterwards that of Lise Meitner appeared. In twenty-six years' time these two were to astonish the world. But already they had proved their worth: born in Frankfurt, Otto Hahn had graduated in Organic Chemistry at Marburg in 1901. He was now thirty-three years old, having been with Sir William Ramsay in London in 1904, with Rutherford in Montreal in 1905 and with Emil Fischer in Berlin in 1906. And here he had stayed. Originally he had intended to become an industrial chemist, but, largely under Rutherford's influence, he abandoned this with immediate success for the study of radio-chemistry—the chemical methods of radio-active research. He had discovered five new radio-active substances: radio-thorium, mesothorium 1 and 2, and, with Lise Meitner, actinium-C″ and thorium-C″. He had demonstrated experimentally radio-active recoil (predicted by Rutherford), and was considered a master of delicate chemical separations.

Things had not always been easy for him. After the return of this 'anglicized Berliner' from Canada, the Rutherford-Soddy decay theory was by no means generally accepted in Germany, and he crossed swords with many an elderly functionary who found him too revolutionary. Yet since 1910 he had been a professor at Berlin University, and now two years later the foundation of the Institute provided the very post he needed for his future work.

Lise Meitner had come to Berlin in 1907. About the same age as Hahn, this small, neat girl had graduated in her native Vienna, and she was now attending a few lectures—chiefly Max Planck's (whose assistant she became for a while)—but was working mostly on radio-activity with Otto Hahn, developing rapidly from his apt pupil into his indispensable helper.

She, too, had her troubles. In the Fischer Institute she could work with Hahn only in the 'wooden workshop' on the ground floor, being forbidden to enter the students' laboratories, so as not to provide a precedent for those campaigning for the emancipation of women. In spite of this, she played a large part in obtaining the newly-discovered mesothorium in pure form, and at the opening of the KWI she had been able to show the Kaiser 100 mg. of mesothorium which she had fractionalized out herself.

Conditions were better in the new Institute: Hahn had three small rooms and a big laboratory, and Lise Meitner was not bothered by prohibitions. Their work centred at this time upon the weak radio-activity of the metals potassium and rubidium, from which many years later the strontium method of determining age by radio-activity was evolved. A gifted young assistant, Martin Rothenbach, also worked with them.

But before their research was finished the war broke out; within three months Rothenbach had died in France; Hahn himself was called up as a sergeant in the infantry. He was soon commissioned and posted to a poison-gas section led by his colleague Haber, so that he was often able to go to Dahlem and carry on at least some of his research on radio-activity.

Lise Meitner was serving as a radiologist in Austrian field-hospitals. Only her few months of leave could be devoted to a new interest she and Hahn were pursuing—yet their work succeeded: protactinium, the missing link between the uranium and actinium series, came to light. This was in 1917; thereafter Lise Meitner was director of the Physical department of the Institute for Chemistry for twenty years, until she was forced to quit the inhospitable country to whose service she had devoted all her energies.

★   ★   ★

In January 1934 the news of the discovery of artificial radio-activity spread across the world: in Paris Frédéric and Irène Joliot had found that the elements boron, magnesium, and aluminium, when exposed to the alpha particles of a radio-active material, emit positrons—and continue to do so *after* the radiation has been cut off. Thus, through exposure to radiation, these elements have formed proper radio-active materials—substances which it would soon be possible to separate out chemically.

There could be no research institute for which this news was so important as it was for the KWI for Chemistry in Berlin-Dahlem. For five years now Otto Hahn had been its director; its Physical department was run by Lise Meitner. Though both were about fifty-five, their scientific vigour and receptivity were unimpaired. Here the most delicate radio-chemical methods were cultivated, and complete separations of imponderable amounts of substances were carried out. Here, then, was the very place to pit radio-chemistry against this new phenomenon of artificial radio-activity.

Otto Hahn was the founder of the 'chemistry of the unweighable'. Up to now, the balance had been the most important instrument of the quantitative chemist. Indeed, Lavoisier's introduction of the balance at the end of the eighteenth century first made chemistry a true science. The balance demonstrated the law of the conservation of mass in the most complex chemical changes; it showed the exact composition of chemical compounds and led to the law of multiple proportions, the first quantitative clue to the atomic structure of matter; it permitted the ever more exact determination of the atomic weights of the elements.

But the sensitivity of the balance is limited. For a long time it sufficed to measure accurately to a milligramme, that is, one thousandth of a gramme. Then that was not enough, and an advance to a tenth, then a hundredth of a milligramme was made. Finally micro-balances were built that reacted to a thousandth of a milligramme—a millionth of a gramme. And then comes a limit. Even smaller traces of certain substances could sometimes be found by spectrum analysis.

Then, with radio-activity, materials were discovered which emit spontaneous and continuous radiation. And the instruments for detecting these rays became so incredibly sensitive that the minutest amounts of these materials could be traced, amounts that lie far below the range of the most sensitive micro-balance, and are reckoned only in milliard or billion parts of a gramme. Not only could these materials be traced, but a technique was evolved for establishing quantitatively their inconceivably small weight from the strength of the radiation.

Was it possible to determine the chemical nature of such tiny traces of a substance? Could chemical changes be carried out with them? Could their chemical properties be identified? Improbable though it may seem, this, too, was achieved. A new science had arisen, the chemistry of unweighable amounts of substances. It deals with minute quantities of radio-active material, and does so with as great assurance as if they lay easily visible to the eye. The chief credit for the development of this new kind of chemistry goes to Otto Hahn and his Dahlem school.

And Hahn himself owed his fortunate series of discoveries to these methods which were largely of his own devising. Now the scope of his work was also enormously enlarged: the discovery of artificial radio-activity brought the hope that radio-active materials would appear throughout the whole system of the elements, not only at the extremity of the heaviest atoms. Perhaps things as yet undreamed of would come to light—and if they did, then Otto Hahn with his well-equipped Institute, his experience, his sixth sense for new radio-active substances, had the best chance of finding them.

★　　★　　★

In less than six months these things were found—but in the Istituto Fisico of the Royal University of Rome, by a man over twenty years younger than Hahn, whose name was nevertheless known to the scientific world. He is Enrico Fermi.

Graduating at the age of twenty-one at Pisa, he spent a year at Göttingen (a stronghold of German physics) and at Leyden, and in 1927, aged twenty-six, he became Professor of Theoretical Physics at Rome University. At once he stepped into the public eye with theoretical works; a model atom bears his name; there followed the theory of the so-called hyper-fine structure, the extraordinarily minute analysis of the spectrum lines, which goes back to the effect of the nucleus. In 1934 he had just sketched out a theory of beta radiation, when the news of the discovery of artificial radiation reached him.

Deserting theory, Fermi now devoted himself to experimental research. With no special resources, no particular experience in radio-activity or radio-chemistry—indeed, with little practical experience at all—he rushed into this difficult field of artificial radio-activity. And something incredible happened: he won the race against Hahn, the old hand. At least, to start with!

He did not tackle this work alone, but gathered together a group of colleagues, whose experience to some extent compensated for his own lack of it. Among them were, first of all, Amaldi and Rasetti, then Segrè, who subsequently, like Fermi himself, emigrated to America. Here also was Pontecorvo, who later took the opposite way and went eastwards to the Soviet Union. The moving spirit of the enterprise, however, was Enrico Fermi.

As soon as he read the Joliot-Curies' report of how they had obtained artificially radio-active materials by bombarding various elements with alpha particles, he determined to attempt the same with *neutrons*. Shortly after Chadwick had discovered the neutron two years before at the Cavendish Laboratory in Cambridge, his colleague, Feather, had used this as an atomic projectile, and had split nitrogen and oxygen nuclei with it. Then William D. Harkins at Chicago University had taken up these experiments, and had achieved further transmutations with neon and carbon. Lise Meitner in Berlin-Dahlem had similarly transmuted nitrogen, oxygen, and argon. True, these had all been 'ordinary' nuclear transmutations, whose end-effect was good stable nuclei again: artificial radio-activity had not yet been discovered! But had these experiments at least shown that the neutron is an effective atomic projectile, capable of producing nuclear transmutations? Could it not also induce artificial radio-activity too?

There was something else in Fermi's mind. So far artificial transmutations had succeeded only with *light* atomic nuclei. Why? Because the missiles used, alpha particles, deuterons, or protons, were all positively charged particles, which are strongly repulsed by the positive nucleus of the bombarded atom; with the energies then obtainable, they could just overcome the weaker resistance of the lighter nuclei, but not the stronger resistance of the heavier nuclei. But, argued Fermi, the neutron, a neutral particle without charge, would not be repulsed either by light or by heavy nuclei; it must surely be able to penetrate the nucleus without needing to force its way through a strong protecting wall, entering heavy nuclei just as easily as light ones. Did this offer the possibility of transmuting all the atomic nuclei, from hydrogen to uranium?

Impelled by this idea, Fermi obtained from a medical colleague a powerful preparation, as much as 800 millicuries of radium emanation (representing nearly a whole gramme of radium!), and enclosed it in a tube with beryllium powder. Thus he had a very powerful source of neutrons. And Fermi also got pure samples of every obtainable element—sixty-eight of them, from hydrogen up to uranium. In the spring of 1934 he started his experiments.

The results fulfilled his boldest expectations: of the sixty-eight elements bombarded, no less than forty-seven became radio-active! And they were elements of every possible atomic number, light and heavy. The lightest element which Fermi activated was fluorine with the atomic number 9, and the heaviest was uranium (number 92). Yes, even the quite heavy nuclei like thorium and uranium could be transmuted to give artificially radio-active materials by neutron bombardment. But wait: surely thorium and uranium are naturally radio-active already? They are indeed. But with neutron bombardment another new, much stronger, and much more short-lived radio-activity is produced. The natural radio-activity of thorium consists in the emission of alpha particles with a half-life of several milliard years; the artificial radio-activity caused by neutron bombardment, however, consists of beta radiation with a half-life of minutes.

Fermi's first publication of 10th April 1934 describes twenty-three activated elements, the half-life of whose radiation he had measured. In rapid succession, there followed over the next year about a dozen articles by Fermi and his colleagues in various periodicals, and what they contained looked like becoming a greater sensation than the mere transmutation and artificial radio-activity of innumerable kinds of nuclei.

First, Fermi found that these artificially radio-active materials without exception emit ordinary beta radiation, that is, negative electrons, in contrast to the elements bombarded with alpha particles by the Joliot-Curies, which give out *positive* electrons—positrons. Fermi found half-lives between 9 seconds and 14 days. Perhaps there were longer and shorter ones, but these were harder to discover.

And then, at the beginning of 1935, Fermi noticed something very peculiar: the activation of many elements becomes much stronger when there is water or paraffin or any other hydrogenous substance near the source of the neutrons. Clearly the neutrons are modified by the presence of hydrogen in such a way as to make them still more effective.

What was the explanation? Fermi, the theorist, at once had the right idea: the neutrons are *retarded* by the hydrogen. The neutrons, arising in the beryllium and being emitted almost with the speed of light, gradually lose nearly all their energy on impact with the hydrogen nuclei. But why should hydrogen have this effect? Because the nuclei of the hydrogen, the protons, have almost exactly the same mass as the neutrons, and hence—according to the elementary laws of impact—can deprive them of most of their energy.

Thus Fermi discovered the 'slow' neutrons. He calculated that these probably have no higher velocity than hydrogen atoms, with which they come into a reciprocal relationship as a result of their natural heat motion: a velocity, then, of only a few miles per second. (This result was later confirmed by the direct measurement of the velocity of neutrons.) And Fermi's experiments also had a result that was surprising and important for future developments: 'slow' neutrons can sometimes be much more effective in transmuting nuclei than 'fast' ones.

Yet this was not the real sensation aroused by Fermi's work. This real sensation had to do with uranium, whose case Fermi found to be especially complicated. Here several new substances are clearly formed, since four different radio-activities with four different half-lives appear. Obviously they must either be isotopes of uranium or else lie a few units lower in atomic number, as had been observed in the cases of other elements. Fermi tried to determine which elements they are. He used the same radio-chemical methods that Hahn had found so successful. In turn, he tested for uranium (92), protactinium (91), thorium (90), actinium (89) and radium (88). The longer he tested, the longer his face grew. The new materials could not be identified with a single one of these elements.

There was but one way to explain this; yet Fermi hesitated to take it. But why should not *completely new* elements have arisen, elements with atomic numbers greater than 92, that do not occur naturally and so cannot be identified with any of the natural elements?

Fermi first published his theory in the June 1934 issue of the English journal *Nature*—that the artificially radio-active materials created by neutron bombardment of uranium are entirely new elements with atomic numbers above 92; that they are trans-uranic elements. This was the sensation! New, trans-uranic elements, which do not occur naturally! Man was building up new artificial elements!

Further experiments in this year and the next brought more material. The concept of the trans-uranic elements gained ground; Fermi ascribed to them the atomic numbers 93, 94, 95 and perhaps even 96 as well. Still, however, he did not succeed in clarifying the details of the problem, in neatly separating the various substances and showing just how they arise. He kept working until he believed that he had solved the problem as fully as conditions at the time permitted. Then he returned to pure theory.

At least the trans-uranic elements had been discovered—so Fermi believed. He did not know that all these elements of his were no more than a fallacy; nor that, in the experiments that led to the 'discovery', he missed by a hair's breadth another, genuinely world-shaking discovery, which would now be made by someone else: Otto Hahn.

* * *

When reports of Fermi's astonishing neutron transmutations and a little later the proclamation of the trans-uranic elements were circulating in the scientific press, Otto Hahn and Lise Meitner had not achieved much. They had been left at the post.

Now they hurled themselves into these neutron bombardment experiments. A new man was working with them; for a few years he had been at the KWI for Chemistry, and his name was to stand beside Otto Hahn's in the final phase of the experiments: Fritz Strassmann. Like Fermi, the three used radium emanation and beryllium as a source of neutrons, though it was less intense than his. Neither did they bombard every obtainable element, but concentrated rather upon the heaviest, which promised the most interesting results: thorium and especially uranium.

Towards the end of 1934 scientific research could not be carried on in Germany without friction. For almost two years the National Socialists had been in power. It might be thought that a pure science like physics could stand aside from politics. But no: the majority of physicists preferred not to interfere, or even to play an active part, in political matters—and this alone rendered them suspect in the eyes of the new rulers. Moreover, there were a few fanatical party members among the physicists: the Nobel prizewinners Phillip Lenard and Johannes Stark, both eminent scientists, became standard-bearers of Nazi intolerance; and soon dissension was rife.

At the ninth meeting of German Physicists at Würzburg in September 1933 Johannes Stark, as the new president of the Imperial Physical and Technical Institute, had delivered a darkly threatening speech, and Max von Laue had courageously broken a lance for freedom by speaking about Galileo, and stressing the parallels with the present.

Then came the persecution of the Jews, the burning of synagogues, the flight abroad of hosts of Jewish intellectuals and scholars. And other freedom-loving men of science, for whom it was possible, also turned their backs upon this barbaric new

Germany. Many who remained were dismissed from their posts. Men like Wolfgang Gaede, who invented the highly efficient vacuum pump, and later Erich Regener, who studied cosmic rays, were thrown on to the street. The world-famous Max Planck himself was hard-pressed; and his son, involved in the resistance to Hitler, later ended on one of the Third Reich's numberless gallows.

Otto Hahn, too, found little favour with the new masters—and certainly not the 'non-Aryan' Lise Meitner! She would soon have been thrown out of a state institution; but the Kaiser-Wilhelm Society was a private association, so that she was protected from the direct power of the state. For the moment Hahn could protect her, and they could continue their work together.

Otto Hahn, Lise Meitner, and Fritz Strassmann worked on the neutron bombardment of uranium. By the end of 1934 they had almost entirely confirmed Fermi's results, and so Hahn subscribed to his thesis that these transmutation products were trans-uranic elements.

Over the following years, Hahn and his collaborators penetrated further into this labyrinth, which proved much more complicated than it had at first seemed. By July 1938 they had established three possible transmutations of uranium, all of which they ascribed to the uranium nucleus U 238 (for natural uranium also contains 0·7% U 235 and a trace of U 234). One of these transmutations is caused by retarded neutrons and leads to a new uranium isotope U 239, which, emitting beta radiation with a half-life of 23 minutes, clearly changes into an element of atomic number 93, thus being trans-uranic. Yet Hahn could not find this trans-uranic element itself. Nevertheless, it is precisely this transmutation which will subsequently attain the greatest significance. The other two transmutations of uranium yield whole series of new substances that can be separated out; Hahn likewise referred to these as trans-uranic elements, and ascribed to them the numbers 93, 94, 95, 96, and 97.

In the course of work extending over four years, there were two events which take the mind back to the distant past of research on radio-activity; at the beginning, in July 1934, Marie Curie died, and in October 1937, in the midst of the work,

Ernest Rutherford followed her. Both failed by a few years to see the decisive moment in the coming of the atomic age.

Another event marked the end of these four years of work—or rather, the dramatic arrival of its final phase. Even Hahn's protection could no longer maintain Lise Meitner's position against the pressure of the Hitlerites; in July 1938 she fled across the Dutch border, and went to Sweden, where she was received by the Nobel Institute in Stockholm. From here she followed with the keenest interest the progress of Hahn's work, in which she had hitherto played so great a part. But in future the research was done by Hahn and Strassmann.

These four years of work had brought out some new facts which go beyond Fermi's findings; yet in the main they had confirmed them. Hahn like Fermi, and indeed the whole scientific world, still believed in the new-found trans-uranic elements. But the turning-point had nearly come.

*   *   *

In other countries work on the neutron bombardment of elements and particularly uranium, had been going on since the publication of Fermi's results. But the same results were not always obtained. In particular, Irène Joliot-Curie and Paul Savitch in Paris raised objections to Hahn's arrangement of the trans-uranic elements in the table of elements in a work published in 1938. They had come upon discrepancies, and had found a further radio-active material of $3\frac{1}{2}$ hours half-life, which behaves like actinium and cannot be fitted into Hahn's decay series.

Hahn and Strassmann therefore carried out new experiments under different conditions, and found that, besides the materials so far observed as arising through neutron bombardment, there are also others—among them the $3\frac{1}{2}$-hour substance of Curie and Savitch—which this time, (in contrast to the trans-uranic elements) could be chemically identified with known elements, and which in fact behave like radium or actinium. The objection raised by Curie and Savitch seemed to be met.

To be quite sure, and because on theoretical grounds it was very strange that radium should be produced in the form observed (the physicists of the KWI had strong doubts about this interpretation) Hahn and Strassmann repeated their experiments with the utmost care in November and December 1938. And something remarkable emerged:

The new substances, which had been taken for isotopes of radium, did indeed behave chemically very like radium, but they showed some small divergences. Yet what could this element be, if not radium? According to their position in the system of elements, none of the trans-uranic elements can behave like radium. But among the known elements the one nearest to radium, and very similar to it chemically, is barium. And its atomic weight is only a good half that of uranium, 138 against 238! Surely such an atomic nucleus could not possibly arise from the uranium nucleus through nuclear transmutation (in which the atomic weight never changes more than a little)!

But still Hahn and Strassmann tested the new substances to see if they could be isotopes of barium. For the first time in these four years, they were testing for an element that is *not* somewhere near uranium in the table of elements. As the tests proceeded the evidence piled up until it became conclusive: every test for barium was positive.

On 22nd December Hahn and Strassmann sent that famous note to the journal *Die Naturwissenschaften*, where they end:

'So we reach our conclusion: our "radium" isotopes have the properties of barium; as chemists we should really say that, with these new bodies, it is a question not of radium, but of barium; and no elements other than radium or barium come into the case. . . . As "nuclear physicists" we cannot reconcile ourselves to this abrupt jump, which contradicts all the experience of nuclear physics up to date.'

Though Hahn and Strassmann may not have been reconciled to it, they had nonetheless discovered the *splitting* of the uranium nucleus by neutrons!

For the product of neutron bombardment they had tested *is* barium. And this radio-active barium nucleus is one of the two parts of almost equal size, into which the uranium nucleus is broken by the impact of the neutron. A quite new type of nuclear transmutation, the splitting of the nucleus, which bears no resemblance to the hundreds of comparatively insignificant nuclear transmutations so far achieved, had become a reality.

Immediately this raised the question as to what happens to

ie energy—for by now the relationship between energy and mass had been thoroughly elucidated. One glance at the mass curve of the elements showed, then, that when a uranium nucleus splits into two fragments of about equal size, a huge amount of energy must be released; an energy which is considerably greater for each nucleus transmuted than in any nuclear transmutation as yet investigated. Indeed, the energy released here could be estimated with fair accuracy: it amounts to 25 million kilowatt-hours for every kilogramme (approx. $2\frac{1}{4}$ lb.) of uranium split! Three million times as much as is released when a kilogramme of coal burns!

A few months later the direct measurement of the energy from the flying nuclear fragments confirmed experimentally this fantastic figure.

This did not, however, mean that atomic energy could yet be harnessed in practice. The billions, the quadrillions of neutrons necessary for the large-scale splitting of uranium by the pound or the hundredweight, and releasing thus the vast energy it represents, were still missing. At that moment perhaps no one suspected how near the solution to this problem was.

But what about the trans-uranic elements, now that uranium-splitting had been discovered? At one stroke, all Fermi's and Hahn's trans-uranic elements were erased from the records of physical science. What had been taken for them was the radio-active remains of the split uranium nuclei, and for four years they had not been recognized as such simply because no one had looked for such 'low' elements; nor had anyone believed that splitting takes place.

The trans-uranic elements had been wiped out. And yet they exist. Before two years had passed, the first of them was *really* to be discovered in America. And it was to transpire that *one* of the interpretations of Hahn and Lise Meitner was correct: the creation of uranium 239 and its transmutation into a trans-uranic element—the very one which they would not have been able to isolate, even with their extremely delicate methods, as it had been produced in too small an amount.

All this was implicit, though mostly unseen, in Hahn's and Strassmann's pronouncement of 22nd December 1938. The observation, trivial in itself, that a radio-active substance present

in minimal traces was barium and not radium, became the mos
important landmark in the development of nuclear physics an
was the gateway to the atomic age; as the avalanche beginning t
sweep down will show.

*   *   *

Otto Hahn's result—barium, not radium—reached Lise Meitne
(now at the Bohr Institute in Copenhagen) by post before it wa
published. She discussed it with her nephew Otto Robert Frisch
also an emigrant from the intolerance of the Reich, and the
immediately arrived at the right explanation of the phenomena
splitting of the uranium nucleus into two almost equal parts; th
release of immense energy as these fly apart. Frisch at onc
began to experiment: he bombarded uranium with neutrons i
an ionization chamber and found the huge ionization impulse
which derive from the great energy of the remains. He was thu
the first to trace these remains by physical methods, and t
measure their approximate energy.

On 16th January 1939, ten days after the appearance of Hahn'
first announcement, two short notes about the Copenhage
findings went to *Nature* in England. Two days later Niels Boh
travelled to America, to a conference of physicists in Washington
He presented the results fresh from Lise Meitner and Ott
Frisch to the astonished conference, before they had appeared i
print. Fermi was also among those present. The circle ha
closed.

At the Washington conference heated discussion of all th
possibilities of the new facts continued into the night. Th
fragments of the uranium nucleus must contain a large surplus o
neutrons. Must it not be supposed that a few new, *free* neutron
may arise, and that these will then split more uranium nuclei
And what then? For the first time the notion of a 'chain
reaction' cropped up. Immense possibilities appeared on th
horizon!

The avalanche swept on. Fowler and Dodson, two America
physicists from the Chemical Laboratory at the Johns Hopkin
University in Baltimore, returned home with the informatio
gained at the conference to their experiments. They also foun
the ionization impulses of the uranium fragments in the ioniza

ion chamber. Their result was telegraphed to London on 3rd February. Thus, in the same issue of *Nature* on 11th February, the first note sent by Meitner and Frisch and the information telegraphed by Fowler and Dodson both appeared. A week later came the second article by Frisch.

The avalanche swept on.

As early as 22nd January, Flügge and von Droste had delivered a manuscript dealing with uranium-splitting to the *Zeitschrift für Physikalische Chemie.*

The *American Physical Review* received the results of Fowler and Dodson on 3rd February.

On 9th February the Vienna Academy, and on 14th February the journal *Naturwissenschaften* learnt that Jentschke and Prankl in Vienna had likewise found the uranium fragments.

By 8th March, Otto Hahn's sixtieth birthday, the avalanche was gigantic; only two and a half months ago it had been started by his simple statement 'barium, not radium'.

On 17th March von Droste found the uranium fragments. He, too, suspected free neutrons. The question recurred: what becomes of the neutrons, which the fragments must contain in abundance? Are there free neutrons?

The answer came on 27th March, when Frédéric Joliot and his colleagues Dodé, von Halban, and Kowarski presented the results of their measurements before the Paris Academy—when uranium is split, new, free neutrons do arise. The assumption was made that these spontaneously split further uranium nuclei, so producing more neutrons and so on, like an ever-swelling avalanche. In this very report the phrase '*réaction à chaine*' occurs.

The magic formula gained currency: chain-reaction. Nuclear chain-reaction. If this chain-reaction of atomic nuclei could be brought about, the defences surrounding the energy of the atom would be broken, and those 25 million kilowatt-hours that are locked in every kilogramme of uranium will be released!

Visions are conjured up of mighty machines fed by uranium, which supply whole countries with light and power; of electricity works running for a year on a single load of uranium; of ships circling the earth on a handful of fuel.

But another, brutal vision overshadows it; one that mocks all that human culture has achieved: it is that of the atomic bomb.

14

THE RACE TO DESTRUCTION

THIS sweeping advance towards the practical application o
atomic energy came at a time of acute political tension.
In those March days of 1939 when the first indication
of the nuclear chain-reaction were appearing in the scientifi
press, Hitler's troops were marching into Prague and occupying
the 'Protectorate of Bohemia and Moravia'. Public opinion and
the official attitude in Britain had stiffened; and behind Britain
stood the more weighty power of America, stupidly belittled by
German megalomania as in 1914-18, but standing ready and
leaving no doubt as to which side her almost inexhaustible
resources would benefit.

Britain would concede no more; Hitler was bent on war
When the German dive-bombers roared over Poland and the
German troops crossed the Polish frontier on 1st September, the
dice had fallen on half a decade of titanic struggle, ending in
chaos and despair.

During the eighteen-day campaign, when the German divisions
demonstrated the first *Blitzkrieg* and soon faced their Russian
'allies' on the demarcation line, while the 'phoney war' left the
western front in peace, remarkable things were happening in
Berlin, at the Kaiser-Wilhelm Institute for Physics (a sister
establishment to the Hahn Institute). A group of eminent
physicists, including Hahn, Geiger, Bothe, Heisenberg, von
Weizsäcker and others, had gathered to consider the problem o
the practical exploitation of atomic energy. Could it be that they
were hatching the atom bomb there?

The German Ministry of War Supply has had disturbing
news from America: leading physicists are said to have been

working with the armed forces for months, preparing the way for the use of atomic energy in the war. Large sums are being spent—can they be building atomic bombs? If America makes the bomb, even though she is not in the war, it will have the same effect as if Britain had made it. And then Heaven help Germany, even if she occupies the whole of Europe by that time!

So the Ministry took over the only establishment in Germany suitable to its purpose, the KWI for Physics in Berlin-Dahlem. Its director, the Dutchman Peter Debye, a Nobel prizewinner in 1936, refused to work for the Ministry of War Supply, and departed. Erich Schumann, a permanent official of the War Ministry and a teacher of the military applications of physics at the University, who was known to be a reliable party member and a good organizer, was made its scientific director. What was to be his first goal—the machine or the bomb?

It was too soon to say, for so little was known: only that the uranium nucleus is split by the impact of a neutron, thereby releasing vast energy. It was known that new neutrons arise in the process, and it was believed that there are more of them than are used in the splitting process; it was thought possible that these neutrons might split further uranium nuclei, and lead thus to a chain-reaction. One other important fact—or rather, assumption—was known. As early as February, Niels Bohr (who explained the shell of the atom in 1913) had expressed the opinion that the various isotopes of which natural uranium consists behave quite differently when the nucleus is split. We remember that natural uranium is composed of 99·3 % of isotope U 238, only 0·7% of isotope U 235 and a tiny trace (0·006%) of U 234. According to Bohr, only the rarer isotope U 235 is split by the *slow* neutrons and could be used in a chain-reaction, while the main constituent, U 238, can be split only by high-energy neutrons, and so is unsuitable for a chain-reaction. In June Bohr, together with Wheeler, supported this view with detailed theoretical arguments; in the spring of 1940 it was confirmed experimentally in America. But Bohr's reputation was such that the German physicists accepted his opinion without further ado.

Nevertheless, a great many problems remained unsolved. Could the U 235 be separated from the natural uranium, or could the latter at least be enriched with the former? How far does the U 238 interfere with a possible chain-reaction of U 235 in natural uranium? How many new neutrons are produced by each splitting process, and what proportion of them is lost in side-processes of the chain-reaction? How could a chain-reaction be controlled, so that it did not develop into an all-destroying explosion?

These were all problems to be solved by the physicists gathered in Berlin, who studied many of them in their individual institutions, though the main experiments were to be carried out in Dahlem.

But conditions were not propitious for the work; Germany, though leading in many branches of science, had fallen noticeably behind in nuclear physics of late years, despite the discovery by a German (Otto Hahn) of uranium-splitting. America, with its vast resources, was now in the lead. Here nearly a dozen big cyclotrons were accelerating projectile particles to huge energies; Germany did not possess one. In the KWI in Heidelberg one was being built, but it would not be ready until 1944. There was a lack of other heavy apparatus, of specially equipped laboratories, and above all of money. The scientists, too, were not over enthusiastic; like the whole German intelligentsia, they had for years been subjected to the contumely of the party, and they were loath to take orders from ill-informed Nazis. Yet there was a war, and the work had to be done, whatever the conditions.

For across the Atlantic America was at work!

*   *   *

At the moment America was doing less than the Germans imagined; but this was to change—for what was being done preluded an avalanche of research such as the world has never seen.

Since the memorable conference of physicists in Washington in 1939, when Niels Bohr reported the latest news from Europe, one man above all had been fostering the idea of increased nuclear research and of an attack on the problem of the atomic bomb. He was not even an American—he was Enrico Fermi, a refugee from Mussolini's Italy, now a professor at Columbia University, New York. Everywhere this small, dark professor was preaching against the fatal dangers of delay. In March he presented himself at the American naval ministry, but the military were sceptical about proposals which were not even based on experiments, and which some experts regarded as mere pipe-dreams.

Yet Fermi persisted; and with his colleague Leo Szilard, he won the support of Albert Einstein for his plans. In July he eventually reached President Roosevelt, to whom Einstein had appealed in a letter. The refugee from Nazi Germany and the refugee from Fascist Italy were now the driving forces which shook America out of a certain complacent calm and set it on the path, which, once taken, was followed with imposing consistency.

'War is imminent', said the refugees, 'Germany, where uranium-splitting was discovered, will not rest until this has been turned to practical account. The Nazis will construct the atom bomb. The Nazis will not hesitate to use it. You can protect yourselves only by anticipating them in building the bomb!' And indeed, the Americans did build the bomb; and they did not hesitate to use it.

President Roosevelt, realizing what was at stake, appointed an advisory commission of physicists and representatives of the army and navy. They decided it was possible to harness atomic energy and to make an atom bomb. In February 1940 the first money—a mere $6,000—was made available, but in November the National Defense Research Council advanced $40,000 to Columbia University for nuclear research over the current year. Then the sums increased like a landslide, keeping pace with the approaching realization of the chain-reaction; and by 1945 the sum of two milliard dollars, amazing even for rich America, was invested in the development of the atom bomb.

The American physicists faced the same problems as the Germans: how could uranium 235 be separated off? Is it possible to start a chain-reaction in natural uranium? What factors inhibit this? For there must be such factors, since otherwise, as there are always a few neutrons about everywhere that could touch off the reaction, every scrap of pure uranium would 'go off' of itself, a self-detonating atom bomb.

How can these factors be obviated? How can the reaction,

once started, be checked? All these questions had to be answered by both the Americans and the Germans, before they could approach the decisive problem: machine or bomb? Naturally, the bomb. But did the way to it not lead through the machine?

This question, too, the Americans had to answer—and time pressed! The Germans had already occupied Norway; in six weeks they had overrun France and forced her capitulation; for a time in the late summer of 1940 it even seemed as if Britain might be the next target. But the Battle of Britain upset German planning, and Britain gained a breathing space which was her salvation. For all Hitler's huge conquests, the issue was still undecided at the end of 1940.

Nonetheless time pressed, and the American physicists had a big programme before them if they were to acquire the atom bomb in a few years. They entered the struggle to solve the problem under good conditions: for years they had been used to scientific team work, money was flowing more freely and they had the most up-to-date apparatus in the world.

These advantages quickly told. In Berkeley, a university town in California, stood a large cyclotron whose accelerator could hurl out protons of 8 M.e.v., deuterons of 16 M.e.v., and artificial alpha particles of 32 M.e.v. of energy. This is seven times the energy of the alpha particles of radium, with which Rutherford made his pioneering experiment. An even bigger machine was already being built, with an electro-magnet weighing 5,000 tons, which was designed for 100 M.e.v., but which an ingenious idea was later to raise to 400 M.e.v. During the war, however, it was to find another use.

Working with the cyclotron was a group of American scientists, among them Edwin Mattison McMillan and Glenn Theodore Seaborg, who would soon be the greatest experts on the trans-uranic elements, and in 1951 would be honoured with the Nobel Prize for Chemistry. Using the cyclotron, they bombarded ordinary uranium with high-energy deuterons. The uranium 238 nuclei that are struck by a deuteron are transmuted, and a new element with an atomic number higher by one—93 instead of 92—is produced. McMillan called it neptunium; it was the first genuine trans-uranic element.

The neptunium isotope Np 238 here created is radio-active. It emits beta radiation, and in a few days changes spontaneously into yet another new trans-uranic element with next higher atomic number, 94: *plutonium*. In this way the isotope Pu 238 is obtained from uranium (though this, too, in unweighable traces recognizable only by their radiation).

Soon afterwards it emerged that similar, but very slightly different, processes take place when uranium is bombarded with neutrons instead of deuterons. It was known that the U 235 nuclei struck are split; on the other hand, the U 238 nuclei hit are changed into a new isotope, U 239. This, too, was known; Otto Hahn found it out in 1937, even before the splitting of uranium.

But now came something new. The uranium 239 is beta radio-active, and changes of itself into neptunium, but this time into Np 239. And this Np 239 is again beta radio-active, and changes spontaneously into plutonium, but this time into Pu 239. This happens within a few days (the first change in a matter of minutes). Otto Hahn had not been able to follow this double change because the amounts of the substance were too small (he had no cyclotron!). Now it could be followed. The plutonium isotope Pu 239, which can be produced simply by bombarding uranium with neutrons, is likewise radio-active, but it lives 24,000 years, and so is for practical purposes a stable substance which can easily be worked with.

Thus, in May and June 1940, while German tanks were rumbling across France, in Berkeley the first trans-uranic elements were quietly born: the elements that Fermi thought he had found years ago, and which led Hahn astray. At first they existed in tiny, unweighable quantities, identifiable only by their radiation. At first. And even their true discoverers did not dream that in a few years plutonium 239 would be produced industrially in a great factory; that it would prove an even more important atomic fuel and atomic explosive than the uranium 235 which now held the field; and that a few pounds of it would wipe out 40,000 people in Nagasaki in a single moment.

* * *

In Berlin, too, they were pressing on with the solution of the two problems: was it possible, by any known method of separating isotopes, to separate uranium 235 from natural uranium? And: how might it be possible to set off a chain-reaction in natural uranium without this separation?

The most effective answer to the first question was offered by the Clusius-Dickel separation-tube process, but this could be used only with gases. There is, however, a gaseous uranium compound, uranium hexafluoride, at normal temperatures a light yellow solid; at 56°C. it evaporates, forming a vapour twelve times heavier than air, which destroys practically every containing material. Now this unpleasant substance had to be mastered; and the outcome was, in any case, doubtful. For the molecular weights of the two uranium hexafluorides, that of 'light' uranium 235 and that of 'heavy' uranium 238, are in the proportion of 349 to 352. Would this small difference of less than 1% be sufficient to separate them in a process which depends upon this very difference in molecular weight?

To bring nearer a solution to the second question, large-scale experiments on the increase of neutrons in natural uranium had to be made. Natural uranium, in which the effective U 235 is diluted to a mere 0·7%, does not of course offer such favourable conditions as would pure or at least more concentrated U 235. And not only the dilution is troublesome. The preponderant U 238 proves particularly awkward, as it snaps up most of the neutrons, which are required to multiply as rapidly as possible, and incorporates them into its nuclei, so forming trans-uranic elements. It was precisely these processes that had just led to the discovery of neptunium and plutonium in Berkeley; and in Berlin at this time Friedrich von Weizsäcker expressed the view that these newly-formed elements might perhaps be more suitable than pure uranium 235 for the chain-reaction. But as the Germans possessed no cyclotron—and to construct a large one takes years—they could not pursue this promising idea further.

So nothing remained but to attempt to render the neutron-consuming uranium 238 innocuous. Careful measurements showed that uranium 238 devours virtually exclusively neutrons of a certain energy, about 5 electron-volts. The neutrons produced by the splitting have a much greater energy, more than a million electron-volts, and so are initially safe. As uranium 235 is split by quite slow neutrons with a fraction of an electron-volt, these new neutrons roam about in the block of uranium, until they have lost nearly all their energy, when they can fulfil their task of splitting a nucleus. But most of them are swallowed up by U 238 nuclei long before.

The only way out of this dilemma was to interpose a special material, a so-called moderator, in which the newly-formed neutrons are slowed down to the energy needed for splitting. Theoretically, hydrogen or a hydrogen compound recommends itself as a 'neutron brake'. Paraffin, a substance very rich in hydrogen, was selected, and nearly seven tons of uranium oxide (later pure metallic uranium was used) were made into a huge pyre with paraffin. The neutrons were measured.

Out of the frying-pan into the fire: the hydrogen certainly slowed down the neutrons rapidly and eliminated the inter-ference of the uranium 238. But it consumed so many neutrons, which were emitted from a small neutron source at the centre, that the whole arrangement decreased, instead of increasing, the neutrons. The first big experiment had failed, and a search had to be made for other materials as moderators.

The physicists thought of carbon in the form of pure graphite, but the results of the experiments were unsatisfactory. Then they fell upon an almost forgotten substance—'heavy' hydrogen, that isotope with doubled atomic weight, which Urey discovered in the year of miracles 1932, and whose nuclei, the deuterons, had since been so widely used in nuclear physics as atomic missiles. Heavy hydrogen can be most easily handled in the form of heavy water, a kind of water in whose molecules the two normal hydrogen atoms are replaced by two heavy ones. This heavy water looks exactly like ordinary water, and behaves similarly, but is some 10% heavier. Towards neutrons, however, it behaves quite differently: it slows them down admirably, and also shows practically no disposition to swallow them up. It is an ideal moderator.

But to construct an 'atomic pile' from uranium and heavy water not only tons of uranium, but also tons of heavy water were needed. For it will not work on a small scale—too many neutrons escape through the surface, before they have time to split a uranium nucleus. So all the experiments had to be on a large scale. But where could heavy water be had by the ton?

Heavy water makes up about one seven-thousandth part of ordinary water, and its separation is a difficult, tedious, and expensive process. It is done by the repeated electrolysis of the water, and requires enormous amounts of electrical power. *One* factory was producing heavy water, the Norsk Hydro at Rjukan in Norway. It produced about ten litres a month. A drop in an atomic pile!

Norway had been in German hands since 1940. The factory was taken over by German engineers and physicists, and production was boosted—by 1941 from 10 to 120 litres a month, and later to over 300. By the end of 1940 the first heavy water reached Germany—only a little, but enough for preparatory experiments. The first hurdle in the race for atomic energy had been cleared.

*   *   *

Ernest Lawrence, the inventor of the cyclotron, was sitting by his 32 M.e.v. cyclotron in Berkeley, which McMillan and Seaborg had recently used to discover the trans-uranic elements neptunium and plutonium. He was considering the problem of separating uranium 235 from natural uranium—the problem that was now, early in 1941, exercising the German physicists.

One method of tackling the problem is with the Clusius-Dickel separating tube (which the Germans tried). Another would be to allow the vaporous uranium hexafluoride to seep through huge porous walls, when, according to known laws, the lighter component containing the U 235 would come through slightly more rapidly. But would the small difference of less than 1% in molecular weight be enough to cause separation in worthwhile quantities?

There was, however, yet another possibility! In mass-spectrographs charged atoms—ions—are separated according to their mass. This is done by sending them through a magnetic field, and then only minute amounts are separated, purely for purposes of measurement. But Lawrence, the master of the mightiest magnetic fields on earth, wondered if this could not be carried out on a large scale. Could not charged uranium atoms be hurtled across a magnetic field, and the U 235 ions, which describe a different path in it from the U 238 ions, be caught separately and in such quantity that a weighable substance accumulates?

This was what occupied Lawrence's thoughts; and if it could be done at all, then the powerful cyclotron magnet in front of him could do it. The poles of this magnet are 94 cm. in diameter! He began to calculate: uranium ions; uranium ion rays; their separation in the magnetic field—it must be possible!

A month later Lawrence was leading a research group working on the magnetic separation of uranium 235. The cyclotron was dismantled and modified, only the magnet remaining and the rest becoming a kind of giant mass-spectrograph. They called the new apparatus a 'calutron' (abbreviated from: California University Cyclotron). Gradually the immense difficulties were surmounted, and if all went to schedule Lawrence should, by the end of the year, be able to separate out one microgramme (one thousandth of a milligramme) of pure uranium 235 per hour.

Was this not a ridiculous enterprise, considering that many kilogrammes are needed for a single bomb? The Americans, however, are optimistic people; they did not give up when the reality lagged so far behind the desire, but set courageously about a task which seemed to present impossible demands.

The Americans, meanwhile, had had the same ideas and made the same experiments as the Germans, and had reached much the same conclusions.

There are three feasible ways of releasing atomic energy:

First the separation of pure uranium 235 from natural uranium —Lawrence was already working hard on this, and the diffusion method would soon be competing as well—and its use in a controlled chain-reaction in an atomic pile, or else directly in an unchecked, explosive reaction: the bomb.

Secondly, the construction of an atomic pile of natural uranium with a moderator. Here the Americans also recognized pure graphite or heavy water as the only suitable materials. They decided in favour of graphite, and used it successfully, in spite of the unfavourable prognosis of the Germans. It was not until later that they built atomic piles using heavy water.

Thirdly, the chemical separation of the plutonium which

must arise in the atomic piles and its independent use in new atomic piles as an atomic fuel—or as an explosive in a bomb.

The first way leads directly to the bomb, the second to the atomic pile, i.e. to the atomic machine, and the third by way of the atomic pile to the bomb. Now the question was ripe for answer: machine or bomb? The Americans made a sensible decision: they followed all three ways at once, letting them compete with each other. Their goal was both machine and bomb.

*   *   *

Again came months of lightning and victorious German campaigns: the spring of 1941 saw the occupation of Jugoslavia, of Greece, and the bold jump across to Crete; but this was the last entirely successful German operation. With the next mouthful that Hitler took, he bit off more than he could chew: Russia.

Few Germans whole-heartedly rejoiced when, on 22nd June 1941, over a hundred divisions began to march into Russia. Most of them remembered Napoleon's downfall. Yet the following months brought many triumphs: vast territories were subdued, and German tanks were already in front of Moscow. Then an early winter held up operations. Of the three main objectives—the capture of Leningrad, the capture of Moscow, and the conquest of the lower Volga—not one was attained. The attempt to run down the Russian colossus in a lightning assault failed.

During this time the German physicists had been doggedly at work. The separation of uranium 235 by means of the separating tube had failed. Other methods were not considered, as diffusion through porous walls was not regarded as hopeful, and no one believed in magnetic separation in a country without experience of cyclotrons. So this way—which was to be the first to lead to the atom bomb three years later in the U.S.A.— was abandoned.

The German physicists, then, redoubled their attack on that other problem—the chain-reaction with natural uranium and heavy water as moderator: the construction of an atomic pile. Research went on not only at Berlin-Dahlem, but also at the ordnance depot at Gottow and in the physics department of Leipzig University.

Further, more delicate experiments were tried with paraffin as moderator, and with metallic uranium instead of uranium oxide. But still the absorption of neutrons by the paraffin was too great, and it seemed that only heavy water had any real prospect. Meanwhile, 150 litres of this valuable substance were available, and production in Rjukan was such that considerable monthly deliveries could be expected. Pure uranium oxide and metallic uranium were being made by the ton by the Auer Co. in Berlin; and in Frankfurt-am-Main the firm of Degussa succeeded in producing the first uranium powder obtained.

In Leipzig, Heisenberg and Döpel were constructing an experimental pile with uranium oxide and heavy water; in it, the uranium oxide—later also metallic uranium—formed concentric spherical layers, and the interstices were filled with heavy water. Inside, right in the centre, was a source of neutrons, a small preparation of radium and beryllium, which emitted its neutrons in all directions. Outside it was surrounded by counters to measure exactly the neutron radiation escaping.

As long as no uranium or heavy water is present, these register the unchanged radiation of the neutron source, but this is modified in two ways when they are present: first, neutrons are absorbed, chiefly by the U 238 nuclei, thus reducing the radiation. Secondly, when the U 235 nuclei are split fresh neutrons are generated, thus increasing the radiation. It all depends which effect preponderates. If an atomic pile is properly set up, the increase must preponderate—the multiplying factor of the neutrons be more than 1. But such an arrangement is still far from being an atomic pile, for nearly all the increase in neutrons escapes outwards. This can be prevented first by enlarging the pile, so that the neutrons will meet uranium further out and most probably split a U 235 nucleus before escaping; and also by surrounding the apparatus with a 'reflector', a covering of heavy water (if necessary ordinary water will serve), of graphite or beryllium, which turns back at least a part of the escaping neutrons.

The way to the atomic pile, then, passes through two stages. First a multiplication factor of more than 1 must be obtained in a fairly small apparatus—without this, nothing can be done. Once it is obtained, the 'critical state' must be reached by enlarging the uranium layers and using a reflector, the state in which, for every neutron that has split a nucleus, precisely one new one is created in the medium for splitting, despite losses by absorption or escaping. In the critical state the artificial source of neutrons is dispensable: the neutrons that disappear through the splitting replace themselves, and the chain-reaction has started.

The various arrangements of uranium with paraffin as moderator had never reached a multiplication factor of 1. The final result had always been a decrease instead of an increase of neutrons. But now the first two experiments in Leipzig at the end of 1941, using uranium oxide and heavy water as moderator, showed that newly-generated neutrons were compensating for the losses of neutrons: the multiplication factor was exactly 1.

The third experiment, in March 1942, was decisive. Metallic uranium replaced uranium oxide; 750 kilogrammes of uranium and 220 litres of heavy water in concentric layers formed a sphere some two-and-a-half feet in diameter. The neutron source was set up in the centre. The Geiger counters began to tick. And the tensely-awaited result was: the multiplication factor was, for the first time, clearly more than 1, it was 1·1. The counters registered some 10% *more* neutrons than the source was emitting; the rate of new generation exceeded losses by 10%. Though this might not be a chain-reaction (as most of the neutrons escape outwards) it nevertheless demonstrated experimentally that this is *possible*.

The German physicists did not know that the same result was to be obtained in the U.S.A. about four months later; they did not know that, at least where the atomic pile is concerned, they enjoyed a lead in the race. But this March 1942 was their most fortunate time; thereafter the speed of their advance was to grow ever slower, while the Americans were beginning to race ahead. By the end of this year 1942 they had a working atomic pile, though the Germans did not have one even at the time of their collapse in 1945.

*　　　*　　　*

On 7th December 1941 the terrible news spread across America that part of the American fleet had been destroyed at Pearl

Harbour. It meant the beginning of the war against Japan. But the Japanese attack brought about the concentration of America's efforts and of her power, and the stiffening of her resolution. And of her atomic projects.

Up to now, atomic research had been carried on by groups at various universities, with little support from the state, though under the general supervision of the National Defense Research Committee and its president, Vannevar Bush. Now there were many changes. Bush first created a special section of the Office of Scientific Research and Development to carry out the uranium programme; to it belonged, besides Bush himself, James B. Conant (later American High Commissioner and then Ambassador in Germany), the physicist A. H. Compton, Lawrence (the inventor of the cyclotron), and Urey, who discovered heavy water.

The preparatory work having been completed, one group from Columbia University under Fermi and another from Princeton were united at a central point in Chicago, where the atomic pile was to be created. In Berkeley Lawrence was working on the magnetic separation of uranium 235, while in New York Urey was working on the diffusion method. Urey, too, was hastening on the production of heavy water.

Lawrence reported the first success: following upon his good results in improving the electro-magnetic technique of separation, it was decided that the gigantic electro-magnet weighing 5,000 tons and with poles of some $5\frac{1}{2}$ yd. diameter, which lay ready in Berkeley at the beginning of the war for a projected giant cyclotron, should also be converted into a uranium separator. In a few months this was accomplished.

The most interesting undertaking had meantime been going on in Chicago. Here—as in Leipzig—the struggle for the multiplication factor of the neutrons was starting. Over there with uranium oxide or uranium and heavy water, here with uranium oxide or uranium and pure graphite.

Uranium was still a bottle-neck in America. On the day of Pearl Harbour there were only a few kilogrammes of it in the whole country, and of this not 50 grammes were of the degree of purity required. The cost of producing pure uranium was reckoned at $2,000 a kilogramme. A year later stocks of pure uranium stood at 6 tons, and every day a further $\frac{1}{4}$ ton was produced, at $40 a kilogramme. The same applied to graphite.

At Columbia University in New York an experimental pile with moderately pure uranium had been constructed; it had achieved a multiplication factor of only 0·87. Could the outstanding 13% be made up by using still purer material?

The experiments continued in Chicago with purer uranium. In May 0·98 was reached. Only another 2%! With the ninth construction in July 1942 Fermi and Allison obtained a multiplication factor of 1·007. They had done it!—but they were not aware that Heisenberg and Döpel in Leipzig had achieved and bettered this decisive result in March.

Now America and Germany were about level in the matter of the atomic pile, of the controlled exploitation of atomic energy. Both had shown the practical possibility; in each case it was only a question of the supply of materials and of outlay as to when the first atomic pile would start operating. And it was in just these matters that American superiority was decisive.

The Americans would have liked to start straight away on building a large-scale construction which would produce energy as an independent atomic pile without an extraneous source of neutrons. But even they could not do it yet, as not enough uranium had accumulated. In the autumn, however, the first layer of the uranium burner was put in place, later to bear the designation 'CP 1'. Thousands of small uranium spheres, together weighing 6 tons, were placed regularly between graphite bricks, until the whole thing was shaped like a huge sphere.

It was easy to calculate that the construction would be finished in the year 1942; and now the eyes of all who knew about the atom project were turned anxiously to Chicago. Would it work?

*   *   *

In the great hall of Harnack House in Berlin a memorable meeting took place on 6th June 1942: the German atomic physicists were conferring with the men in charge of armaments.

Though the scientists remained the same, there had recently been a re-organization among the atomic physicists. The uranium project had been put under the control of the Reich's

Research Council, under the direction of Abraham Esau, president of the Reich's Institute for Physics and Technology.

In charge of German armaments was Hitler's architect, Albert Speer, who was not very enthusiastic over his appointment to the Ministry of Munitions in the middle of the war, after the death on 8th February 1942, of his predecessor Todt. But his lack of enthusiasm for his post did not prevent his being sentenced to twenty years' imprisonment in Spandau at the Nuremberg trials. Now, after four months in his responsible office, he and his staff faced the atomic scientists and had to decide on the continuation of their plans for their secret work.

The war situation in general had become fluid again. Rommel and the Afrikakorps had pushed on nearly to the Egyptian frontier; a new German offensive on the eastern front was making good progress. But still the lower Volga had not been reached, nor yet the dark turning-point of Stalingrad.

And there were disturbing indications: the British and American saturation air-raids on German cities were beginning; only a week before the first thousand-bomb attack had fallen on Cologne.

All this must have been in Speer's mind as he heard the reports of the various groups of physicists, which were summed up by Esau:

It seemed hopeless to try to separate out uranium 235, so that the best way to the atom bomb was blocked. The atom bomb might be reached by way of the atomic pile and the production of plutonium; but the prerequisites for research along these lines were lacking in Germany.

With the atomic pile itself, however, successful progress had been made. In March the neutron multiplication factor 1 had been exceeded in Leipzig, and it would be raised still further. It could therefore be regarded as certain that a self-sustaining chain-reaction was attainable: that the construction of an energy-producing atomic pile would succeed. Although to develop it industrially would cost much time and money.

Such was the summary of three years' work. Now Speer had to take his decision; he decided that the quest for the atom bomb should be abandoned, and the atomic pile project pursued on a limited scale.

This—at the turning-point in the war—was the turning-point in the German uranium programme.

*   *   *

A few months later there was intense activity in the U.S.A. The whole atom project was proceeding under the code-name 'Manhattan District', and close liaison had been established with the army, Brigade-General L. R. Groves having been made responsible for the military side.

In Chicago Fermi was directing the building of an atomic pile, whose graphite bricks and uranium spheres rose up layer on layer. At its base was a neutron source, and Geiger counters kept constant check on the increase in neutrons.

The means had long since been found to prevent the nuclear chain-reaction, the explosion, from getting out of hand. A material is simply introduced into the device that consumes as many neutrons as possible, so inhibiting their action (whereas the other substances used consume as few as possible). For this the metal cadmium is very suitable, as its hunger for neutrons is many thousand times greater than that of heavy water. Rods of cadmium are therefore fixed so that they can be pushed into or drawn out of the graphite-uranium block. The insertion of the cadmium rods unfailingly halts any chain-reaction.

During construction the rods are left in, being withdrawn only for the regular neutron counts. Towards the end of November, these checks showed an extraordinary increase in the multiplication of neutrons: the critical state was approaching. On 2nd December, even before the previously calculated size was reached, it was there: as the cadmium rods were gradually withdrawn, the Geiger counters began to tick—without any artificial source of neutrons!

Rather taken aback, the physicists and engineers stood beside this great block, inside which the miracle was happening: the first nuclear chain-reaction—inaudible, unseen, known only from the ticking of the Geiger counters. Here a continual release of atomic energy was taking place, the conversion of atomic energy into heat; the amount of energy released depended solely upon the position of the cadmium rods, upon how strongly the process was artificially retarded. And the physicists were very circumspect, allowing the atomic pile to run at only half a watt to start with. Only after exhaustive checking and measuring for ten days did they withdraw the rods a little further and advance to 200 watts. This was as high as they dared go yet. Two years later, in the Hanford Works, atomic piles were running with a total output of about 1 million kw.

So the atomic pile was functioning, and an atomic machine could be built: a boiler could be heated with this 'uranium fuel' and a steam-turbine driven. But what of the atom bomb?

Now that it was possible to set off a chain-reaction, the atom bomb must also be possible. There was a simple recipe for it: instead of natural uranium, take *pure* uranium 235 (or pure plutonium 239). Tons of it are unnecessary, perhaps 10 kilogrammes would do. Remove the moderator (and, of course, any cadmium!)—and the atom bomb is ready.

And the detonator? There is none. The few starting neutrons are present everywhere, either from the cosmic rays or from the very weak 'spontaneous splitting' of uranium that had meantime been discovered. The atom bomb, then, goes off of itself, without any detonator. What! Of its own accord? Then it could not be produced!—But it could: in two parts. Each part must be smaller than the minimal size that leads to the chain-reaction. By themselves, the two parts are harmless. You can hold them; throw them on the fire; hit them with a hammer; explode detonators on them—it makes no difference. But the moment the parts are suddenly brought together, it is all over. The effect is that of 20,000 tons of T.N.T.

One detail, however, was still missing—the pure uranium 235 or pure plutonium 239. It was to take the next two years to provide this detail and it would devour 90% of the whole outlay of 2 milliard dollars. Now, in the autumn of 1942, before the atomic pile in Chicago was working, while in Europe the outcome of Stalingrad was becoming clear, while Rommel was being driven back at El Alamein and the Americans were landing in North Africa, during those turbulent weeks the foundations of all the atomic developments of future years were being laid. Three huge buildings were being planned.

The first was at Oak Ridge in Tennessee, where the Clinton Works were to have three tasks: the industrial separation of U 235 by Lawrence's calutron method, its separation by the uranium hexafluoride gas diffusion method, which had meanwhile been developed, and finally the running of a 1,000 kw. atomic pile as a pilot plant for plutonium production.

As Oak Ridge did not seem sufficiently isolated for the large-scale production of plutonium, another vast undertaking was planned: the Hanford Works on the Columbia River in Washington State, in the extreme north-west near the Grand Coulee power works.

Besides industrial plant, a big new research centre was needed for the development of the atom bomb—somewhere utterly isolated from the world, yet with the most modern equipment. A table-mountain in New Mexico, 30 miles from Santa Fé in the inhospitable south-west of the States, was chosen. There the atom city of Los Alamos grew up from nothing; and there the man would work who, though in the background now, was to lead the last phase of the research: J. Robert Oppenheimer.

Including the atomic pile centre in Chicago, a huge net of atomic installations covered the whole country. By air, Los Alamos is some 1,200 miles from Chicago, while it is nearly 1,900 miles from Oak Ridge to Hanford. So far this net existed only on the map—but from now on the invisible machinery which was to give it life would run unceasingly.

*   *   *

The Norsk Hydro Works lie in a ravine near the village of Rjukan in Norway. With a head of water of two thousand feet, over 660,000 gallons a minute (once Norway's biggest waterfall) are piped to giant turbines which develop 400,000 h.p.

Here, protected from air attack by towering mountains, the mysterious heavy water is made. From here some 200 to 300 litres of this precious substance, indispensable to the German atomic pile experiments, leave for Germany each month.

The turbines run day and night. On the night of 27th February 1943 only their drone can be heard—except for the steps of the German guard, as he disappears round the corner just after midnight.

The snow lies in the pale moonlight. Is there a movement of muffled figures? They are already at the gate; there is a faint rattle, as the chain is cut by wire-cutters. They slip into the yard, and up to the basement door. It is locked. The figures vanish into the tunnel where the cables enter the building. All is quiet, but for the drone of the turbines. Ten, twenty minutes pass; then, suddenly, the figures appear at the end of the tunnel, and run for their lives. Flames are already shooting up. Stones and metal rattle down; a dull explosion echoes along the ravine, then another and another.

The guards run out, shots crack out in the darkness.

But the endless forests have engulfed the nine men of the Norwegian resistance, who—after months of training on a model of the building in England—have been parachuted in and have been living for a week in a nearby mountain hut until the time came to carry out their plan.

The irreplaceable separation plant is a heap of ruins; a thousand litres of heavy water pour back into the element from which they were taken. The only source of the German atomic scientists' most vital material is cut off.

Later an attempt to re-start production was made. An air attack prompted the decision to transfer the whole plant to underground workshops in Germany.

But the valuable consignment, together with the heavy water obtained in the meantime, was never to reach Germany. On a February morning in 1944 it landed at the bottom of Lake Tinusjo, sunk during the crossing by a time-bomb smuggled aboard by the Norwegians.

★   ★   ★

In March 1943 Robert Oppenheimer went to Los Alamos. He was Professor at the University of California in Berkeley, a colleague of Lawrence, McMillan, and Seaborg. But while they were experimentalists, he was a theorist. He was only thirty-nine, he lived for his science, and could be extremely absent-minded, which might seem no great qualification for the director of a large research undertaking, demanding insight, decisiveness, and organizing ability. But time would prove the justice of his appointment, and he would easily solve the hardest problems facing him.

Oppenheimer had started learning his physics at Harvard, had continued his studies in England and Germany, where in 1927 he took his doctorate at Göttingen University. Then and for many years he showed Communist sympathies, which, ten years later in the witch-hunt of 1954, were to cost him all his appointments and offices relating to atomic research.

Los Alamos was originally a bunch of wretched buildings on a plateau surrounded by deep canyons, accessible from Santa Fé by a winding mountain road. It had nothing—nowhere to work, no instruments or equipment, an inadequate power supply, not even accommodation for the scientists.

Six months later it was transformed; it had become a neat little town with houses, shops, schools, everything. And the laboratories! Month after month lorry-loads of the most modern equipment had arrived from all over the United States. Los Alamos now boasted a cyclotron, two van de Graaff generators, a Cockcroft and Walton high-tension plant, and a great deal of other valuable apparatus.

In Los Alamos Oppenheimer assembled the elite of physicists. Many worked there permanently, some temporarily. Fermi and Bohr could be seen there, the American physicists Bacher and Allison, the Englishman Chadwick, the theorist Bethe—a refugee from Germany—, the chemists Kennedy and Smith, and many more. And Klaus Fuchs, who later betrayed his secret information to the Russians, was also among the initiate.

Research at Los Alamos centred on the problems of the atomic bomb. However simple this may be in principle, many details needed investigation before a major trial could take place. The work was broadly based, so that the ground was also prepared now for much that looked beyond the trial explosion and the end of the war to the future.

Meanwhile great factories were rising at Oak Ridge, the Clinton Works, really three separate factories in three different valleys. The three were to have distinct tasks; in the first an atomic pile grew up. It was not a low-power unit of 200 watts, like that in Chicago, but was five thousand times as powerful, giving 1,000 kw. Even so, this plant was regarded as experimental, the first for obtaining plutonium. Later on, in Hanford, the output was again to be raised a thousandfold.

The second factory was designed for the electro-magnetic

separation of uranium 235 from natural uranium. There dozens
of those huge cyclotron-like magnetic machines which were
developed in Berkeley under the name calutron were assembled.
The advantage of this procedure, as opposed to building an
atomic pile, that must first be complete as a unit, was that each
individual machine could be brought into service as soon as it
was finished, instead of having to wait for the completion of
the next one or even of the whole plant. It is true that the daily
yield of such magnetic separators is not as much as one milligramme of U 235, and many machines must work for years to
produce any worthwhile amount of the desired isotope.

The third factory was to separate out U 235 by diffusion of
gaseous uranium hexafluoride through porous walls. The idea
is simple: the lighter isotope passes through the pores rather
more quickly, emerging enriched on the other side. Looked at
quantitatively, however, the yield is hopelessly little, unless
hundreds, even thousands, of separating walls are used, which
together must have an area of many acres; for to obtain 99%
pure uranium 235, the gaseous uranium hexafluoride must pass
through a separating wall not less than four thousand times over.

While the separation of uranium 235 both magnetically and
by gas diffusion had been tried successfully at least on a small
scale, the production of plutonium in an atomic pile broke new
ground. Plutonium, the second of the trans-uranic elements,
was discovered only in 1940, and its existence finally established
in 1941. At first it was the isotope 238, but soon it was *the*
plutonium isotope 239—the only one usable in a chain-reaction,
and hence as an atomic explosive (fifteen years later thirteen
isotopes with atomic weights from 232 to 246 were known!).
By August 1942 only $\frac{1}{2}$ milligramme of plutonium 239 had been
produced; the only possible method of production at the time,
the bombardment of uranium with neutrons from the cyclotron,
did not permit larger amounts to be made. Nonetheless, plans
were now drawn up for the production of plutonium by the
pound by means of an atomic pile, from the (not yet attained!)
chain-reaction. The only intermediate station on the way to
large-scale production was to be the experimental pile at the
Clinton Works at Oak Ridge. Production itself was to be carried
on at Hanford.

The amount of plutonium produced in an atomic pile is proportional to the energy produced. A 1,000 kw. pile can produce a few milligrammes of plutonium daily; to raise this to a few kilogrammes daily, atomic piles with a capacity of about 1 million kw. must be built. This would have been a sizable power station at the same time. But as the utilization of the accruing energy would give rise to an enormous amount of development work, consuming time and money, it was not exploited. It was not energy, it was plutonium, it was the bomb that mattered. All this enormous energy, then, had to be harmlessly disposed of, so that it did not make the piles white-hot. To do this, the biggest cooling system the world has seen was devised: the ice-cold waters of the Columbia River were pumped through the piles.

In the atomic pile the uranium is continually enriched with the newly-created plutonium. The last task, then, is to separate out the plutonium. But that is more or less child's play compared with the separation of pure uranium 235. For plutonium is a different chemical *element* from uranium, and not only another isotope of the same element. Hence it can be separated by established *chemical* methods, eliminating any trouble with calutrons or diffusion walls. But the separation department at Hanford was still a factory of considerable size.

Towards the end of the eventful year 1943, the situation was this:

At the Clinton Works—which a year ago had existed only on paper—the first calutrons had been assembled in March; since September some of them had been working and separating out the first uranium 235.

In June a huge steam-power plant, one of the biggest ever built, had been begun in the gas diffusion division. Further installations followed in September, but it would still be some time before this department was in production.

The pilot atomic pile for testing plutonium production had been started in February, and had been working at 500 kw. since 4th November. Soon this would be raised to 800 kw., and in May to 1800 kw.

In Hanford the giant works were growing up, which were to be built and run by Du Pont de Nemours, America's biggest chemical trust. Three gigantic atomic piles, for reasons of safety many miles apart, were planned. Since September the first had been in operation—and plutonium production had begun.

*   *   *

At the beginning of 1944 there were some 2 tons of heavy water in Germany; there could be no more from Norway, and with German industry overtaxed and air-raids growing more devastating, a new heavy water factory could not be built in Germany.

Would 2 tons be enough for an atomic pile? Calculations—which might deceive in a subject of which so little is known—suggested that they may.

Walter Gerlach, famous for the delicate Stern-Gerlach experiment, which first showed the magnetic moment of atoms, had taken over direction of the atom project from Esau. The main research was being done in Berlin jointly by the Berlin and Heidelberg KWI for physics; it was done in an air-raid shelter of the Berlin Institute, where the many raids passed almost unnoticed.

Over nine trial piles in Leipzig, Gottow and Berlin the neutron multiplication factor had been lifted from 1·1 to 3. Now three times more neutrons were leaving the uranium and heavy water device in the shelter than the neutron source at its centre delivered. This device was reaching stately proportions: in a magnesium tank with 1½ tons (1,400 litres) of heavy water were seven layers of metallic uranium, 1¼ tons of it. This was surrounded by a 10-ton graphite casing, designed as a neutron reflector; and already it had improved the multiplication factor considerably. But still the pile was some way from the critical state, the independent chain-reaction.

Calculations indicated that progress might be made firstly by increasing the size of the pile, and secondly by using a large number of smaller, 2-inch uranium cubes instead of relatively fewer, compact layers. With this in mind, it was decided to build a new experimental pile.

In February 1944 the Hahn Institute for Chemistry was destroyed in an air-raid. Even though the shelter provided some protection, work in Berlin became increasingly difficult; the power supply and communications were repeatedly interrupted, and there were many other obstacles. It was time for evacuation.

Evacuation was the catch-word of those hard months. Away from the dangers of the battered cities to the camouflage of the forests and the mountain valleys! Playing hide-and-seek with destruction! The German arms industry had continuously increased production into 1944 by large-scale evacuation, in spite of the rain of bombs. It was the civilian population that perished by the hundred thousand in this terror from the sky.

So the evacuation of the KWI for physics began. Part of its equipment went to the little south German town of Hechingen, to await re-assembly in a brewery; the uranium department waited its turn. For the moment the construction of the pile that might have achieved the desired chain-reaction was halted.

But the transport problem worsened: other undertakings had priority. Without support, atomic energy research remained a wretched pretence, with no real chance of success.

On 6th June the Allies landed in Normandy: the long-awaited invasion had begun. Slowly, bitterly, the German defences were pushed back, until the dam broke and the conquering flood poured across France and Belgium, reaching German territory at Aachen on 13th October. Here the advance was held up, but it was no more than a breathing-space of a few months for the Germans, whose collapse could no longer be averted.

In the shelter at Dahlem the uranium cubes, the heavy water, and a few physicists were still waiting for transport to south Germany, hoping to snatch at success in the twelfth hour.

*　　*　　*

By the beginning of 1945 a sense of victory prevailed in America. The last desperate German offensive in the Ardennes had failed; on 7th March Cologne fell, and soon afterwards American troops crossed the Rhine. From the east, the Russians, having regained their lost territory and Poland, were spreading over German land—though this might not have been exactly welcome to all the Americans. In any event, the total collapse of Germany was only a matter of months—*without* the atom bomb.

But America still had a hard nut to crack: Japan. Germany's collapse had spared her the atom bomb; not so Japan's resistance.

The military planners already reckoned the atom bomb as the final weapon in this war. Were they right?

The bomb, indeed, was all but complete. But could a process that had never taken place be predicted with absolute certainty? In a few months the physicists would have made the bomb, but not one of them could say with complete assurance that it would work.

Never had such huge undertakings, such vast resources been invested in a plan which existed solely on paper, which had not been realized on a small, experimental scale—because it is impossible: this plan staked all on the success or failure of a major trial.

The experiments at Los Alamos were approaching their conclusion. By the middle of the year there would be enough fissionable material for three bombs, two with uranium 235 and one with plutonium. One of these, a uranium bomb, would be tested; if this went off, the others would too.

A regular exchange of information had meanwhile been going on between Los Alamos, the big atomic works, and other research centres. In Berkeley, Seaborg and his colleagues had made a discovery which, though of no direct effect on the development of the bomb, opened up interesting prospects for future atomic research. Seaborg bombarded plutonium 239 (atomic number 94), of which there was a sufficient supply for all kinds of experiments, with artificial alpha particles of 40 million electron-volts from the cyclotron. This gives rise to a new element with an atomic number higher by two, that is 96. Soon afterwards, he had also found the element belonging in the gap thus created at 95. Two new trans-uranic elements had been discovered; the element 95 was named americium after the native land of its discoverer, and the element 96 keeps green the memory of Marie Curie, the great pioneer, with the name curium. The further development of the trans-uranic elements had nothing to do with the bomb, but crowned a purely scientific endeavour initiated many years before by Fermi and Hahn.

Another development, which had to do with the bomb, was, however, just beginning in Los Alamos, though it was to be years before it matured. One of Oppenheimer's closest colleagues was Hans Bethe, a theorist like himself, director of the theoretical division of the atomic laboratory, a German by birth who was now in American service. Bethe made some stir in 1938, when he—at about the same time as the physicist von Weizsäcker in Berlin—elucidated the nature of the chain of nuclear reactions which, as we have to-day good reasons for thinking, has been heating the sun for milliards of years, and which explains the huge energy continually radiated into space by the sun, a fraction of which falls upon our earth with all-important results. This enormous energy is released ultimately by hydrogen nuclei uniting to form helium, four hydrogen nuclei to *one* helium nucleus.

This work of Bethe's had been inspired by discussions with Gamov and with another physicist, Edward Teller, a Hungarian Jew who had fled to America just in time to escape the Nazi concentration camp. Now, in 1944, Teller was also working in Bethe's department at Los Alamos. He was a rather difficult colleague, who did not fit easily into the laboratory team, but followed his own ideas. A favourite idea of his was the fusion of hydrogen nuclei. He may well have wondered whether this could be achieved on the earth when the discussions about the production of the sun's energy were going on. But at that time not even uranium fission was known; now the first atomic explosion was about to be realized, and he could not rid his mind of the thought that the uranium 235 or the plutonium, both very difficult to produce, might be replaced by the cheap hydrogen.

Teller calculated. It was soon clear that ordinary hydrogen was unsuitable. But there was heavy hydrogen; and not long ago 'super-heavy hydrogen' had been found,—tritium—a most peculiar, slightly radio-active material. Ordinary hydrogen has the atomic weight 1, heavy hydrogen 2, and tritium 3. There is practically no natural tritium—in the whole, seemingly infinite volume of the earth's atmosphere there may be a total of a few litres; but through nuclear processes it can be made, though in the first place only in tiny amounts.

The calculations showed that, with a mixture of heavy hydrogen and tritium, an energy-producing reaction should take place, if this mixture were heated under pressure to an initial temperature of 50 million degrees C.; and, said Teller, we can reach this temperature if we have the atom bomb. With this we can 'spark off' as much of a suitable hydrogen mixture as we want.

With this idea, Teller fathered the hydrogen bomb, the H-bomb, which is vastly more destructive than an 'ordinary' atom bomb. Not Teller alone, of course; for to realize such a conception the concerted work of many minds is necessary. But at this time in Los Alamos a development began which, having lain dormant for some years, eventually became a terrible reality.

At the moment, however, it was not a reality but an idea. But it was a reality that the last deliveries of uranium 235 and plutonium were arriving from Clinton and Hanford, and that the bombs were being built; every detail, every possible source of interference was checked over a hundred times.

Then, on a stormy night, the finished bombs set off along the winding mountain road—to be tested operationally.

★　　★　　★

Haigerloch is a picturesque little place in the foothills of the Swabian Alps, near the seat of the Hohenzollerns. In the spring of 1945, Haigerloch had a carefully-guarded secret instead of its usual tourists: in a cellar carved from the cliff was the last German atomic pile, the materials for which had in the end been brought there, and assembled by a group of physicists—Fritz Bopp, Erich Fischer, Peter Jensen, Oskar Ritter, and Karl Wirtz. They were mostly young; and their labours were in a lost cause, in respect of both the war and the object of their research.

As to the war: the Americans had pressed on from the Rhine; the Russians were marching on Berlin; hostile aircraft were flying around unmolested. At any moment must come the end of Hitler, and of the Reich.

And the research: did the German physicists suspect what mighty atomic weapons America had now constructed? In spite of strict security, something of it had penetrated even thus far. In the August 1944 issue of the *Physikalische Blätter* could be read: 'In the United States scientific research is being carried out on a new bomb. The material used is uranium. If the forces contained in this element should be released, explosive effects of unimagined power will be produced.'

Though they knew that the end was near, the German physicists in this cellar at Haigerloch had used the experience gained at the last attempt in Dahlem and built an improved pile

A ton and a half of metallic uranium in 680 2-inch cubes were arranged at regular distances in a tank with $1\frac{1}{2}$ tons of heavy water. The tank was 1·4 metres in diameter, 1·6 metres high and was surrounded by a layer of graphite blocks weighing in al 10 tons. The whole thing was then sunk in an aluminium boiler of more than 2 metres in diameter and height, with ordinary water. Inside were the neutron source and, in many different places, measuring instruments.

And the result?—Twice as good as in Berlin! Almost seven neutrons were finally achieved to *one* from the source. The chain-reaction had not started, but calculations showed that, by increasing the diameter and the height by 15% the critical point must be reached. But the material for these enlargements was lacking. Somewhere in Germany was another half-ton of heavy water, and there might have been some uranium; but in April 1945 there was no hope of getting it.

And so the German atomic pile—on the verge of success— remained a torso.

On 22nd April Allied troops entered Haigerloch; immediately afterwards, American specialists appeared and took possession of the materials and equipment.

Germany was out of the race.

* * *

In the small hours of 16th July 1945 a thunder-storm rages over the Alamogordo desert. A barren plateau extends for miles around, bordered in the distance by bare mountain ranges From the centre of the plain rises a steel mast 100 feet high You might take it for a wireless mast, if you did not know that its top held the most dangerous thing in the world—the first atomic bomb, due to explode in a few minutes; that some fifty pairs of eyes are gazing through a system of mirrors at this one point, that, in shelters some 6 to 10 miles away, fifty nervous systems are torn with tense expectation.

When at precisely 5.30 a.m. a blinding, radiant ball of fire rises over the desert, when a shattering crash rolls across the plain, when a monstrous, unparalleled column of surging, livid cloud shoots some seven miles into the sky—then the tension

the fifty witnesses of this epoch-making event is relaxed; they
el a complete enervation, whether it be General Groves or
mes B. Conant, the President of Harvard University, whether
be Vannevar Bush or Enrico Fermi, whether Oppenheimer
some anonymous technician or photographer.

At this moment they are all capable of only one vague thought:
e calculations were correct. The great trial has succeeded.

Three weeks later the places where the Japanese cities of
iroshima and Nagasaki once stood were desolate expanses of
bble and ashes. For the first time in the world's history two
mbs had broken a brave people's resistance.

The war was over.

*   *   *

ut was the race over?

Most races attract spectators. Here these were the Russians.
spite of the devastation caused by the German assault, of
eat losses in men and materials, the Russians had nevertheless
atched with growing interest over the years what was going on
the field of atomic research.

The Russians possess some good physicists: they have, for
stance, S. I. Vavilov, Abram Joffe, and Jakov Frenckel. And
jotr Kapitza, once a pupil and an assistant, and later director
f a department under Lord Rutherford at the Cavendish
aboratory, had prolonged permanently an intended short visit
Moscow in 1934.

Since the capture of Berlin the Russians can call on the ser-
ices of a few more good physicists—for example, the Nobel
rizewinner Gustav Hertz, Manfred von Ardenne, and many
thers.

The Russians, moreover, have an excellent espionage service.
ommunists all over the world supply them with information;
nd some of the most valuable they received from Klaus Fuchs
nd his accomplices.

So at the end of the war they knew what was happening.

The differences between Russia and the west had already
ecome irreconcilable: in to-day's allies could be seen to-
orrow's opponents. And so began a new race for the power of
e atom—not now between Germany and America, but between

America and Russia. America had a few years' lead: and th
time the race was to keep the lead, not to reach the winning-pos
America tried to keep ahead; Russia to catch up. Milliards o
roubles flowed against milliards of dollars.

These were the auspices under which the world, after th
greatest and most terrible war of its history, entered upon th
'peace'.

15

TOWARDS THE ATOMIC AGE

O N 7th May Germany capitulated unconditionally; on 17th August Japan followed. The fighting was over. But no peace treaty was concluded—and in ten years' time it would still not be concluded! 'Peace' meant no more than the end of the bombing, of the black-out. It meant that twice-ravaged eastern Europe, great tracts of Russia, of Poland, of Rumania were left as depopulated deserts, with shattered towns, razed villages and the scorched earth marking the path of the fury of war. War had twice spilled across the breadth of France, in 1940 the German, in 1944 the American invasion. In Britain many cities, and especially London, bore the cruel scars of the German *blitz* of 1940 and of the V 2's of the last months of war.

The devastation stretched from the North Cape to Africa.

But nothing equalled the centre of Europe: Germany!

Over three years, about one million tons of T.N.T. had hailed down on her towns; not one large town, and only a few of the smaller ones, were not in ruins; 50,000 people perished in ten days in air-raids on Hamburg in 1943, and 250,000 in that single night of 14th February 1945, in Dresden.

Was there any Germany left?

Her richest eastern regions were annexed by Russia or were under Polish administration, and the rest of the country was divided into four occupation zones. The occupation rested heavily on the German population, swollen by millions of refugees from the east. Allied troops maintained order only in so far as it affected their own security, feeling called to carry out the American 'Morgenthau Plan'—the destruction of Germany for decades to come.

Millions of German soldiers were in prisoner-of-war camps, and many millions of German men, women, and children were starving in their impoverished and ruined country; the old, the ailing, the infirm were dying under the burden.

In these years, too, death reaped a rich harvest among the men of science: in 1945 Hans Geiger, inventor of the atomic counter, died in Potsdam; in Munich Wolfgang Gaede, who devised vacuum pumps; in Potsdam in 1946 Werner Kolhörster, an expert on cosmic rays; in Nesselhausen in 1947 Philipp Lenard, the master of electron rays; and in Göttingen Max Planck, whose quantum theory established a new conception of the world. Old though he was, he had managed to escape from an estate near Magdeburg before the advancing Russians to spend his last two years in poverty here.

Otto Hahn was more or less a prisoner in Britain, where he learnt from the newspaper that he had been awarded the Nobel Prize for Chemistry in 1944—for the discovery of uranium fission, which formed the basis of the atom bomb!

The German Physical Association and the Kaiser-Wilhelm Society for the Promotion of the Sciences had been dissolved; German research was at a stand-still.

A first small stirring of new life came in the summer of 1946 with the formation of the German Physical Association in the British Zone, which soon had parallel but separate organizations in the other zones. Eventually, on 26th February 1948 the new Max Planck Society, with the institutions of the old Kaiser-Wilhelm Society, was called into being in Göttingen. Otto Hahn, long since back from Britain, became its president, and Werner Heisenberg the director of its Physical Institute.

But this did not revive German science. The institutes were bombed, equipment lost; industry was only just able to begin making small deliveries, and the state had no money. And over and above this, German research was in the strait-jacket of the notorious Control Commission regulation No. 25: all scientific research was under strict allied control, and whole branches of research—among them experimental nuclear research—were prohibited.

And so, for the next ten years, there was no German research in the atomic field.

Things were very different on the other side of the Atlantic. As in 1918, America was the only power to emerge unweakened from the struggle; once again as in 1918, but to a much greater extent, the centre of research moved to the land of unlimited possibilities.

Only Russia could achieve anything comparable. Through the war her power had been extended to the Elbe, and during the war she had subordinated every civilian consideration to the building, with American aid, of a huge armaments industry; now she poured vast resources into scientific research. And from being an ally, Russia had become America's most dangerous enemy. The scientific work she was doing remained hidden behind a hermetically sealed wall.

America still felt secure in the knowledge that her industrial potential was greatly superior to that of her Russian competitor. She still had the monopoly of the atom bomb, and—the experts said—it would take Russia at least fifteen years to catch up.

So America scaled down her military research and laid the emphasis on peace-time industry and pure science. And pure science could now profit from four years of war-time exertions—including those of her opponents. There was, for instance, the rocket proving-ground at White Sands in New Mexico; here lay the silvery bodies of countless German V 2 rockets, brought as war booty. Perhaps the only field in which Germany had gained a lead in the war was to become the basis of a new weapon in the American arsenal: the rocket. For this purpose not merely a few dozen missiles in working order had been shipped to the States, but so had their German creator, Wernher von Braun.

Almost every week a rocket traced its fiery path across the New Mexico sky. And not only the military had the opportunity to probe the secrets of rocket ballistics, of remote control, of homing, and much besides; no, a number of rockets were made available to various research groups for purposes of pure science.

Before long there were photographs of the earth from nearly a hundred miles up, showing the rounding of its surface; there were measurements of the earth's magnetic field from far outside its atmosphere. There were investigations of this atmosphere, of its highest layers, its density, pressure, temperature. There were measurements of all kinds of rays, taken so high up that they are not weakened or falsified by the deep sea of air.

Rays! What were the rays found up there? Not only all of those coming from the sun—light, heat, ultra-violet, even X-rays —but also all those streaming in from space: the cosmic rays.

The first V 2 rocket equipped with counting-tubes ascended on 28th June 1946, and others followed.

From the results automatically radioed back to earth, the scientists found a completely constant radiation from a height of about 35 miles to about 100 miles. This is the primary cosmic radiation, still free from the secondary radiation set up far below in the atmosphere. Perhaps the last lingering doubt as to their cosmic origin was removed.

*   *   *

Meanwhile in the Hanford Works in Washington State the three great atomic piles continued day and night with the mysterious process of transmuting elements. How envious the old alchemists would be, if they could but see!

Uranium changes into neptunium, neptunium into plutonium. And beside the value of this, that of gold is insignificant. But beside the curse of plutonium, the curse of gold is insignificant: plutonium is the charge in the atom bomb!

So Hanford produced its daily quota of a couple of pounds of plutonium, and gradually the American stock of atomic bombs grew; for it was to deter any aggressor. The million kilowatts of energy released went to waste in the Columbia River, the cooling system; the neutron radiation, which could be used for interesting experiments, was absorbed by a concrete wall a yard thick.

Research, however, had its turn—for there was yet another nuclear reactor. There was the CP 1 in Chicago, the first reactor to go into service during those exciting days of December 1942. By now it had a brother, the CP 2, also built of natural uranium and graphite as moderator.

Near Chicago is the Argonne National Laboratory, and now a third reactor, the CP 3, stood there; it had heavy water as a moderator, as the German physicists had tried years before in Dahlem and in Haigerloch. Heavy water has the advantage over graphite that it slows the neutrons down far more quickly; hence heavy water reactors can be built smaller than graphite

reactors: CP 3 used 3 tons of uranium to the CP 2's 50! Six tons
of heavy water against 500 tons of graphite! Unfortunately its
difficult separation process makes heavy water very expensive—
a quart still costs several hundred dollars.

And there was the 1,000 kw. trial reactor at the Clinton Works
in Oak Ridge, which was also available for research.

In Los Alamos, too, work on an entirely new type of nuclear
reactor was proceeding. Was it possible to use enriched or pure
uranium 235 or even plutonium, as in the atom bomb, for a
nuclear reactor? Would it not be feasible to dispense with the
moderator (the neutron-consuming uranium 238 being absent),
and to use fast instead of slow neutrons, as in the atom bomb?
The reactor can be prevented from emulating the bomb by
cadmium rods. And such reactors with highly concentrated fuel
could be quite small, having a few pounds of uranium instead of
many tons.

Several such plans were maturing in Los Alamos. The
'homogeneous' reactor was already working, the 'water boiler',
where all the energy is produced in a solution of a uranium compound in a steel sphere a foot across. The 'fast neutron reactor'
came into being; it was no bigger, and had no moderator, using
instead pure uranium 235 or pure plutonium.

Yet another plan was mooted: why should only the few
thousandth parts of uranium 235 contained in the rare and
valuable uranium be used? For plutonium can be made from
the large residue of uranium 238 with the neutrons accruing
from the fission of the uranium 235. If as much, or possibly
more, plutonium could be obtained than uranium 235 is consumed, then the atomic pile would continually create its own
fuel, until all the uranium 238 had been used up. Now there
was a new target: the 'breeder reactor' must be developed, one
that produces its own fuel!

Gradually the development spread to other countries: in
Canada, at Chalk River in Ontario, a large nuclear reactor of
10,000 kw. output sprang up; in France a smaller reactor was
set up at Le Chatillon near Paris; and several were rising in
England. Apart from military installations at Sellafield in Cum-
berland, an atomic centre was established at Harwell in Berkshire.
There the first reactor GLEEP (Graphite Low Energy Experi-

mental Pile) of 100 kw. was built, to be followed by BEPO (British Experimental Pile) of 4,000 kw. output.

All these piles were to subserve scientific research, and simultaneously to produce as large amounts as possible of radio-active isotopes, the era of whose extensive use was just dawning.

For the time, no one contemplated producing industrial energy; three years after the end of the war, electrical energy was nowhere being won from the atom. People still hesitated to pick the ripe fruit.

★   ★   ★

The atomic piles afford scientists neutron rays of unsuspected strength: inside the great blocks of uranium are streams of neutrons of many billions of particles per square centimetre per second. Those emitted, however, are mostly slow neutrons with an energy of a fraction of an electron-volt. But a lot can be done precisely with these slow neutron rays of high intensity. They change most elements into radio-active isotopes; they penetrate thick layers of solid materials; like gamma rays, they cause physiological damage; in crystal lattices, they show interference as the electron rays discovered by Davisson and Germer in 1927 had done. Beside X-ray and electron interference, neutron interference now became the object of study, and a neutron spectroscopy developed.

But all this does not displace high-energy *charged* particles. Before the war, the record for 'artificial alpha rays' from the cyclotron had been 32 M.e.v. of energy. With the giant magnet (of 4·7 metres diameter), though it was temporarily used to separate uranium isotopes, it had been intended to break the 100 million volt barrier.

This intention, however, was anticipated. Immediately after the war the General Electric Company had come forward with a machine delivering 100 M.e.v. *electrons*. The machine is a so-called electron-thrower, a betatron, whose principle goes back to Rolf Wideröe (whom we met when the cyclotron was conceived), and whose actual construction to the American, D. W. Kerst. High-energy electrons have little effect on nuclei; but, when they strike a metal screen, they produce X-rays of correspondingly high energy quanta. And these 100 M.e.v. X-ray quanta (with 100 times the energy of natural gamma quanta!) prove effective for all kinds of nuclear transmutations, splitting even the heaviest nuclei.

At first there had been some trouble with the cyclotron. With energies of the order of 100 M.e.v. or more, protons and other similar particles increase their mass quite perceptibly, as a result of relativistic mass increase. This makes their rotation slower than the accelerating high-frequency warrants, they 'fall out of step' and gain no further acceleration.

Hence there was some doubt about attaining 100 M.e.v. deuterons in the new giant cyclotron at Berkeley; but progress was not to be delayed for long. In 1945, directly after the war, Edwin McMillan in Berkeley, one of the discoverers of the trans-uranic elements neptunium and plutonium, and simultaneously a Russian named V. Veksler, suggested how the difficulty could be overcome: the frequency of the alternating voltage which accelerates the particles in the cyclotron, instead of remaining constant, must be lowered to match the slower rotation of the particles.

This is the principle of the synchro-cyclotron: it opened the way to energies of any magnitude. Its application to the existing giant cyclotron showed its effect. In 1946 it broke all records with deuteron streams of 200 M.e.v. and artificial alpha rays of 400 M.e.v.

McMillan extended his idea to the acceleration of electrons, and this mixture of the betatron and cyclotron principles proves effective—that is, the use of rotation fields, which is successful in the betatron, coupled with acceleration by means of high-frequency electricity fields. But, since with the light electrons the relativistic mass increase is more noticeable than with the heavy protons, deuterons, or helium nuclei, a change of frequency, which was so effective in the synchro-cyclotron, is not enough here. The magnetic field which causes the bending of the path of the particles must also be made variable. Thus another machine came into being, and in 1947 at Berkeley McMillan could put the GEC apparatus in the shade with 300 M.e.v. electrons.

But this was not the end: the synchrotron principle, the precisely controlled variation of the magnetic field, makes it practicable to keep the radius of the particles' circuit constant during the whole acceleration process. Why, then, use vastly expensive, compact electro-magnets? Now an annular magnet, adapted to this constant circuit, would do! And an annular magnet can be made ten or a hundred times bigger!

Plans to cross the 1,000 M.e.v. barrier with gigantic proton synchrotrons were made; in 1947 the foundations of two such mammoth accelerators were laid in the U.S.A., both for protons. The first was for the newly established Brookhaven National Laboratory near Upton on Long Island, where a monster atomic pile of 28,000 kw. output was already building. As its particles would reach the energy of cosmic rays, it was called the 'cosmotron', and would give protons of 3,000 M.e.v. The other, still larger, project was for Berkeley; its name was 'bevatron'— its goal 6,000 M.e.v.

Years, however, were to elapse before the two giants were in service.

★ ★ ★

In spite of all the successes recorded by pure research, the armed services still had the greatest resources to draw on. Their annual dollar budget ran well into the milliards. For a year the guns had been silent—but not the forges of the arms factories.

In the Pacific Ocean, almost on the equator and roughly half-way between Hawaii and New Guinea, lies a typical south-sea archipelago: the Marshall Islands. The numberless islands, stretching for hundreds of miles, had been sighted by mariners in 1526, but were not re-discovered until two and a half centuries later, by the Englishmen Marshall and Gilbert. At the close of the nineteenth century their main town, Jaluit, was the centre of a Hamburg trading enterprise, and by 1885 the Marshall Islands formed part of the German colonial territory.

After the First World War they were promised to Japan; and in the second American soldiers wrested them from the Japanese in particularly bloody battles. Now, in 1946, when they again come into the ken of history, they lie as the troops left them, a waste of shell-holes and bomb-craters.

One of these islands is called Bikini, a coral reef with a big lagoon. As yet it is hardly on the map—it has not yet blasted its way into the general consciousness with atomic explosions; nor has its name (for some mysterious reason) been carried round the world by a scanty female bathing garment.

Bikini: a south-sea island—it must have been a paradise. Once. To-day it is an army camp. To-morrow all hell will be let loose here.

The American forces have long been looking for a suitable testing ground for atom bombs; they thought of the sea, of the Marshall Islands, of Bikini. Here there is room for new tests— the effect on ships; explosions under water; trying out new bombs.

On 1st July 1946, at nine o'clock in the morning, the fire-ball of an atomic explosion again rises into the stratosphere. It stands over Bikini, as a year ago it had stood above the desert of Alamogordo, and then above the nightmare scenes of Hiroshima and Nagasaki.

Three weeks later, on 25th July, the fire-ball again appears over Bikini. This time it is an under-water explosion. The column of water which rises from the lagoon is half a mile wide and over a mile high. More than ten million tons of water have been hurled into the air by a few pounds of atomic explosive.

The results—the 50,000 photographs and the 300-mile film-strips of 'Able Test' and 'Baker Test'—have been analysed. The explosive effect of the first trial bomb of Alamogordo, the standard bomb, had been as great as that of 20,000 tons of T.N.T. Only fifty of these standard bombs would suffice to equal the total effect of the many millions of bombs that hailed down on Germany during the whole war. But the Bikini bombs are more powerful than the standard bomb!

The armed forces are satisfied. And slowly the growing stock-pile of atom bombs is added to the American arsenal.

*   *   *

Things were not quite so warlike everywhere. Britain, it is true, was making atom bombs, and one of the next fire-balls was to rise over the Australian desert. But in 1947 Britain put herself at the head of peaceful atomic research with two discoveries of new particles in cosmic rays.

At an interval of only two months, the sensational reports appeared in the same journal *Nature*. A group of scientists comprising the Englishman Frank Powell, the Italian G. P. S. Occialini, and the Brazilian C. M. G. Lattes, working at Bristol University, made its report; and in December two Englishmen, G. D. Rochester and C. C. Butler from Manchester University, made theirs. Both groups reported the discovery of new elementary particles.

Should we still call these fleeting and extremely unstable visitors to our world of particles, which were first exemplified in the meson of Anderson and Neddermeyer in 1938, elementary particles? It started even with the neutron. It is now known that this, too, is not a proper, stable particle, but changes on average in 19 minutes into a proton and an electron; but 19 minutes is virtually an eternity for an atomic particle. In 19 minutes an electron in the hydrogen atom has completed $7\frac{1}{2}$ trillion rotations —two milliard times more than our old world has made since it came into being.

Was not the positron also unstable? Not really; certainly it likes to disappear, though only when it meets an electron, united with which it is annihilated. Left to itself, the positron would not change.

But Anderson's meson! After only a few millionths of a second it is gone, leaving behind a miserable electron (or positron, according to whether it was negatively or positively charged). The particles recently discovered in England were of this extremely transient kind—even more transient, although this was not at once clear.

Now even unstable particles must have a name. Powell aligned his as the Pi-meson with Anderson's Mu-meson; for they are closely related: when the Pi-meson decays, a Mu-meson is left. Rochester and Butler tentatively named their particles V-particles. Pi-mesons exist with positive and negative charge; a few years later neutral ones were also found. V-particles seemed from the first to exist both electrically charged and neutral. What are their other characteristics?

The Mu-meson (according to later, exact measurements) has 207 times the mass of an electron.

The (charged) Pi-meson has 273 times the mass of an electron.

And what is the mass of the V-particle? What remains when it decays?

So far that was uncertain. The V-particles owe their discovery to some strange 'events' in the Wilson chamber. Their discoverers could only say that their mass must be fairly large, perhaps as large as that of the proton and certainly much greater than that of the Mu- and Pi-mesons. And the decay product? Still less certain!

The following years were to show that the V-particles are a species of a large group of particles whose mass is of the order of that of the proton, even a little greater, and that they decay in the most varied ways, giving rise to a proton and a Pi-meson, or a neutron and a Pi-meson, or something else. To-day we call this group of heavy, unstable particles hyperons.

Soon there was to be a swarm of new elementary particles, or, as the American Morrison jocularly called them 'non-elementary particles'. Could it really be only twenty years since there were merely an electron and a proton, and then a positron and a neutron?

Yet at that time the V-particle had not betrayed its hydra nature. It had simply been discovered—and by the Wilson cloud-chamber method, which was not altogether new, and which also brought to light the Mu-meson and the positron.

The Pi-meson, however, owes its discovery to a brand-new method of observation, which thus began its triumph. This is the photographic plate.

But this is, at bottom, the oldest observation method of nuclear physics. The first act of the drama, Becquerel's discovery of uranium radiation in 1896, is written on a photographic plate. Then, however, only the general darkening of the plate was used to trace radiation and to measure its strength quantitatively.

Later it was noticed that the plate, when suitably set up, could also indicate the direction of the radiation, that, for instance, a radiation star appears on the plate from the point of a radio-active needle, caused by the alpha particles which shoot out in all directions. But the marks of the individual particles were too blurred and unreliable to be very productive.

In 1937 the Vienna physicists Marietta .Blau and Hertha Wambacher obtained for the first time on photographic plates, which they exposed for months to cosmic rays on the Hafelekar, 5,500 feet above Innsbruck, traces of cosmic ray particles, and even 'stars'—photographs of exploding nuclei, whose components fly in all directions. Thus the photographic tracing method entered cosmic ray research. But much remained to be done, and it was ten years before the Englishmen could record their success.

They had to work for many years. The trouble with ordinary plates was that the sensitized coating is too thin, and most particles pass out of it too quickly. And worse: this coating is too coarse-grained. The problem was not solved until the Ilford and later the Kodak companies developed special so-called nuclear plates, with a gelatine coating several millimetres thick and of exceedingly fine grain.

Such plates are simply laid for a few weeks on a high mountain or sent up to great altitudes by balloon. Afterwards they show hundreds of thousands of interesting tracks of high altitude radiation particles, which need only to be analysed under a microscope. *One* plate replaces a milliard tentative Wilson pictures, by far the most of which show no tracks. On the other hand, the analysis of the results is a laborious business.

Plates like these, left for a month at some 18,000 feet up in the Bolivian Andes, caught the Pi-meson, the new member of the family of particles.

Then the scene changes back to Berkeley in America, with its giant cyclotron. Lattes, one of the discoverers of the Pi-meson, had joined an American, Eugene Gardner, there. Could not Pi-mesons, which are knocked out of nuclei by cosmic particles of very high energy at great heights, also be created by artificial high-energy particles—perhaps the 400 M.e.v. alpha particles of the cyclotron?

They could. Early in 1948 Gardner and Lattes found first negative, and then positive Pi-mesons when the 400 M.e.v. alpha particles struck all sorts of materials—beryllium, carbon, copper, uranium. They found so many that the cosmic radiation mesons pale beside them. The Pi-mesons decay, as they should, leaving Mu-mesons; so now artificial Pi-mesons could be produced directly, and artificial Mu-mesons indirectly.

The new age of meson research had come!

*　　*　　*

All this time there was no research in Germany. The economy was ruined; the people were hungry; the black market flourished. Money had lost its value.

Nonetheless, everyone worked doggedly to preserve his primitive existence. And reason registered a victory on 1st January 1947, with the fusion of the American and British occupation Zones into a unified economic area; one at least of the senseless zonal borders, that could be crossed only after obtaining a permit, disappeared. But the French and especially the Russians stood upon their separate rights.

Gradually the Western Powers' mistrust of all things German changed into a willingness to help, there were the beginnings of co-operation. And on 20th June 1948 came the currency reform! Though imposed by the occupying powers, it was for Germany's own good. For a moment, every German, beggar or millionaire, was equally rich—or poor: each one had the sum of 40 of the new D-marks, the new currency that was to stabilize the economy. It was the shot that started the race to success, marking the turning-point in Germany's wretchedness. There was food again, and goods to buy with a stable market-value.

A mighty new industry sprang up—the 'German miracle' was starting; in a few years the worst scars of war had healed. The D-mark was among the strongest currencies of the world.

On 8th May 1949 the foundation statute was proclaimed; on 7th September Western Germany was united in the Federal German Republic.

Only one zonal frontier now existed—the Russian; and day by day it was strengthened and became an 'iron curtain'. Behind it, Moscow's puppets proclaimed the German Democratic Republic.

In the Federal Republic a surging new economic and industrial—and scientific—life began to emerge. There were new scientific achievements. But none in the field of nuclear research, of atomic energy research: inexorably, Control Regulation No. 25 remained in force.

*   *   *

But atomic research was flourishing elsewhere, in Britain, above all in America.

In 1947 the Canadian Chalk River reactor, the 'NRX', a big heavy water reactor of 10,000 kw. (later 30,000 kw.), came into operation. It long held the record for the strongest neutron radiation in its interior: 50 billion neutrons per square centimetre per second. Five years later it was to achieve a melancholy fame when, through a servicing fault, it exploded; but miraculously no lives were lost.

The first fast neutron reactor, 'Clementine', began to function at Los Alamos in 1949: a small experimental reactor of only 10 to 25 kw., but one which first ventured to use fast neutrons, like those in the atom bomb, instead of slow ones. Its fuel was pure plutonium, and it was cooled by mercury. Yet it, too, was pursued by ill fortune: four years later it had to be dismantled because a crack in the casing of one of the plutonium rods caused the mercury to become radio-actively contaminated.

Los Alamos also continued the experiment with 'homogeneous reactors', which work with a solution of a uranium compound with enriched U 235 uranium. The first tentative attempt, the 'Lopo' with less than one watt output, was followed by the 'Hypo' with 6 kw., and in 1951 by the 'Supo' with 45 kw. output. It was still small; but new paths were being trodden, and who knows?—perhaps the future lay with the homogeneous reactors.

Meantime at the Brookhaven National Laboratory the giant reactor BNL, of the standard type with 60 tons of uranium and 700 tons of graphite, had been built. It is four storeys high, and at each storey a gallery runs along the great concrete wall, making all the control points, the numberless gauges, the apertures for inserting probes and materials accessible to the maintenance staff. The heat output of the BNL is almost 30,000 kw., but this is blown away by air-cooling—some two and a quarter million gallons of air per minute. The reactor weighs 20,000 tons, and it cost 20 million dollars to build.

With the X 10 at Oak Ridge, the BNL reactor served mainly to produce radio-active isotopes on a large scale. Here was an alchemists' factory, actually carrying out the transmutation of elements. And those whose work exposed them to the dangerous radiation looked fantastic enough: muffled up in clumsy 'atom suits' with lead to protect them from the gamma radiation, they manipulated long tongs to take the spiteful substances out of the magic furnace and despatch them to a place of safe keeping. Everywhere counters checked the intensity of the radiation. Strict regulations prevented injury to health through exposure to radiation above the permitted dose.

A new concept had developed: these men called the strongly radio-active materials 'hot' substances. Generally these came in an impure state from the pile, and had to be separated and purified. The many processes used for this were known as 'hot chemistry'. The greatest care was essential! Woe to him who would touch such material with his finger! Rubber gloves, even big tongs were not enough; the highly concentrated substances were checked, stored, diluted, removed only in sealed rooms behind concrete walls a yard thick. They were handled by a complicated system of steel arms and hands, which were controlled from outside: so-called manipulator slaves. These artificial hands were observed by a system of mirrors. Thus man protected himself from the murderous attack of those very substances that he had just called into being.

From here the radio-active isotopes, suitably diluted but still carefully packed in lead-lined boxes, were sent to their destinations. The number of these boxes grew year by year: between 1946 and 1951, fully 1,000 curies of radiation equivalent, equal to more than a whole kilogramme of radium, were devoted to the treatment of cancer alone, in the form of radio-active iodine, radio-active phosphorus, radio-active gold—with a total value of over a million dollars. And this was a mere beginning.

Other reactors were built: the CP 3' in the Argonne laboratory, the LITR and the BSF at Oak Ridge, the two latter using almost pure uranium 235.

Then two especially interesting reactors were built: the EBR (Experimental Breeding Reactor), designed to carry out the idea of breeding new atomic fuel, and the MTR (Material Testing Reactor), which, with highly intensified neutron radiation, was to test all kinds of materials for their resistance to this radiation, and hence their suitability in the construction of reactors.

These two reactors were built in a new place—the township of Arco in mountainous Idaho in the north-west of the U.S.A., at the newly established reactor experimental station. Both were fuelled with small amounts of nearly pure uranium 235, yet they were of high output: the MTR, with only four kilogrammes of uranium, reached an output of 30,000 kw.—more than the Brookhaven reactor with its 60 tons! It also dethroned the NRX in Canada: with 400 billion neutrons per square centimetre per second it attained eight times as intense a radiation.

The MTR came into operation in 1952, the EBR, like 'Clementine' working on fast neutrons, as early as 1951. Its task was to discover the conditions under which a reactor breeds as much, or more, fuel than it consumes; on 4th June 1953 Gordon Dean, Chairman of the Atomic Energy Commission, was to inform the world that its task had been fulfilled.

And the Experimental Breeding Reactor had yet another peculiarity: through its cooling-system flowed a liquid alloy of sodium and potassium. This transferred part of its energy to water in a heat exchanger, and steam was produced; at 30 atmospheres it drove a turbine, and this drove a 250 kw. electrical generator. The light of the well-lit reactor building derived from the split uranium nuclei!

A big bronze plaque indicates the beginning of a new age: 'Here on 20th December 1951 electric current was first generated by means of atomic energy.'

It was not yet ten years since the astonished physicists in Chicago first saw the miracle of a self-maintaining chain-reaction. Six years before the fire-ball over Alamogordo showed the instantaneous release of gigantic energies. Now the spell was broken: atomic energy could be used for industry. The atomic machine had been born.

What follows is rather an economic than a technical problem. Would it pay its way? Could atomic energy be produced as cheaply, or more cheaply, than the energy from coal, oil, or water power? Would it be able to compete with the traditional sources of industrial energy?

Years, perhaps decades, of experience must give the answer; as yet the costs of building and maintaining an atomic power station were too uncertain.

At the time, however, one authority was greatly interested in atomic energy, whether it was economic or not—the American navy. Did it not offer the very solution to the problem of submarine propulsion? The atomic machine is the only machine that can work with practically no fuel and no air at all! Submarine voyages of any duration became a possibility.

Soon, therefore, the keel of an atomic submarine was laid down, and shortly afterwards of another. In co-operation with the Atomic Energy Commission, two big firms, Westinghouse and General Electric, were set the task of developing atom-driven power units of several thousand horse-power.

The mechanical exploitation of atomic energy was about to become an imposing reality.

*   *   *

Meanwhile events of the greatest importance had been taking place in another sector of the now vast atomic field.

August of 1949 had brought the United States the alarming news that the Russians, too, had the atom bomb!

A B29, flying a scientific mission over the north-west Pacific to investigate cosmic rays, had suddenly found radio-active traces of an atomic explosion. British aircraft confirmed the finding. The kind of radio-activity even suggested that the Russian bomb was of a fairly highly developed type.

The American politicians fell out of their rosy optimism. The experts on Russia had assured them they had a lead of at least fifteen years in the construction of the atom bomb. It was only four years since Alamogordo—and America's bomb monopoly was broken!

President Truman summoned the National Security Council. Plans for cutting the defence budget were torn up; the country's efforts had to be redoubled: a 'position of strength' must now be the political objective.

And so, carried on behind the scenes for a long time, began one of the most violent and relentless internal struggles of post-war American history: the struggle for the hydrogen bomb.

The idea of using the energy developed by the fusion of the lightest nuclei for a hydrogen bomb dates back to 1945, indeed, to earlier discussions between Gamov, Bethe and Teller arising from Bethe's theory of the sun. But in the summer of 1945 Edward Teller of the theoretical division at Los Alamos had written a memorandum about the H-bomb.

The basic idea of the hydrogen bomb is this: when light nuclei—for instance those of ordinary hydrogen, or better, of deuterium (heavy hydrogen) or tritium—unite to form heavier ones, very high energy is released, as nuclear bombardment tests had shown; this energy is of a magnitude similar to that released by the splitting of the uranium nucleus, or rather more per kilogramme of substance used. But the light nuclei do not fuse so very easily; they do so only when they collide with great force, and this happens on a sufficiently large scale only when the mass to be fused reaches a temperature of 30 or 50 or 100 million degrees Centigrade. It is impossible to calculate exactly, and much depends on the mixture employed. Probably it could not be done with ordinary hydrogen; with deuterium, only when tritium is added to it. Now, the production of a litre of tritium cost several million dollars. And nobody could say definitely whether the reaction would really take place, if the attempt were made to reach the necessary enormous temperature by incorporating an 'ordinary' atomic bomb as a 'detonator'. The great majority of nuclear experts were convinced that it could *not* be done.

Against this, the H-bomb, if it were feasible, promised to eclipse the A-bomb as an instrument of destruction. For an A-bomb can be built only up to a definite maximum energy, as amounts of uranium or plutonium above this 'critical size' would explode spontaneously. But the H-bomb knows no limit: any amount of hydrogen or deuterium or tritium can be piled up without fear of a nuclear explosion, as the temperature to set it off must first be generated by the detonation of an A-bomb. So it appeared possible to make hydrogen bombs with an effect a hundred, a thousand times that of the Hiroshima bomb: a threat of terror and devastation passing all imagination.

This was Teller's idea. He had always been one of the few who believed that Russia had made swifter progress than was generally thought, and was making A-bombs, if not H-bombs. 'There are', said Teller, 'only two alternatives: either we make the H-bomb, or we wait until the Russians drop it on us.' Was not the situation similar to that involving Germany in 1939?

Teller, however, found little sympathy for his scheme from

the new director of Los Alamos, Norris Bradbury. Many of his scientific colleagues, believing the H-bomb project to be Utopian or wishing to have nothing to do with any intensification of the atomic horror, rejected the idea. Teller was called a warmonger, and the plan stagnated for four years.

But now, after the early detonation of 'Joe 1', the first Russian atom bomb, things changed; Teller, followed by those few who had lent their support to his plan, began his dogged up-hill struggle against the majority of the scientists, of the military, and of the politicians. His greatest opponent, the spiritual leader of the anti-H-bomb faction, was one of the outstanding men of nuclear science—the maker of the first atomic bomb: Robert Oppenheimer.

The persons of these two contestants are also interesting. Both are of Jewish extraction, neither is of old American stock. A native German, Oppenheimer's father had emigrated to America when he was seventeen, and had established his position as an importer of textiles in New York. Teller, born in Budapest, the son of a Hungarian lawyer, had come to America by way of Germany only in 1933. They contrast in appearance: Oppenheimer, aged forty-five, is lean, with a small, intellectual face, rather dreamy eyes and lightly greying hair. Teller, four years younger, looks more robust with his round face, his shock of dark hair, and eyes looking from under thick, dark brows.

At first the struggle went against Teller. A committee of the Atomic Energy Commission including Oppenheimer, Fermi, Rabi, and Conant (who soon left to be High Commissioner in Germany) decided firmly against the H-bomb.

Then in January 1950 Klaus Fuchs, who had worked for a long time in Los Alamos and then at the Harwell atomic centre in England, and who knew all the atomic secrets including the H-bomb plans, confessed that he had betrayed his knowledge to the Russians. As the danger increased, so Teller's stock rose.

By 31st January President Truman acted: he announced that the hydrogen bomb was to be built.

Still few scientists believed that it would function. So the struggle went on. The military feared a weakening of the American position by the diversion of immense resources and valuable atomic material from the A-bomb to the H-bomb project. For every gramme of tritium, 80 grammes of plutonium had to be sacrificed. There was general obstruction, and Teller saw his hopes fading.

But in July the Korean war broke out. Antagonism to Russia grew. And so at last a first major trial with a 'thermonuclear reaction' was planned for early in 1951. Many backed the idea simply to reduce the H-bomb to absurdity through an unsuccessful test.

Once more the Marshall Islands, this time the Eniwetok group, were chosen for the trial. It was not really a bomb that was to be exploded, but a 'device': a shapeless frame-work on a tower, containing an A-bomb surrounded by a mixture of various kinds of heavy hydrogen in a liquid state (because of the higher density)—that is, supercooled to 250°C. below zero! It was a monstrosity, utterly unsuitable, in its present form, for use in war.

But this was to see if it would work in principle—if the exploding A-bomb would draw the hydrogen into the nuclear explosion or not. Would the moment before everything shatters be long enough? Or would the 'tinder' burn out before the 'fire' caught?

When, in May 1951, the blinding ball of light irradiates Eniwetok from above, the very first impression proves that the experiment has succeeded. The improbable has materialized: man has brought to the earth the blazing fires of the sun's interior, the elemental fusion of hydrogen nuclei!

The analysis of the results showed that the boldest expectations as to the amount of hydrogen exploded had been far exceeded. About one hundred times the energy of the Hiroshima bomb had been released.

This May morning over Eniwetok has seen energies unleashed at a single blow that are greater than the explosive energy of the sum of the bombs dropped over Germany in four years.

After the successful Eniwetok test, Oppenheimer and his followers ceased all further opposition; Teller had won.

The epilogue to Oppenheimer's opposition to the H-bomb came years later, when his attitude rendered him politically suspect. His left-wing past, his (long since evaporated) sympathy for Communism were dug up, he was even accused of being a Soviet agent, and in December 1953 he was suspended from all his offices.

McCarthy, the Communist-hunter, took a hand; an investigating committee examined over forty witnesses in six weeks. And Oppenheimer was cleared of the charge of treason, but not of having delayed by his attitude the construction of the H-bomb. His dismissal from the service of the state was recommended.

The Atomic Energy Commission, whose Chairman Oppenheimer had been for four years, approved the decision by four votes to one. So in July 1954 we see Robert Oppenheimer once more as a professor at the Princeton Institute of Advanced Study, as a colleague of Albert Einstein, back in the post he had left eleven years ago to found the atom city of Los Alamos.

*   *   *

The advance towards the atomic age is still gathering momentum.

The radio-active isotopes enjoy their triumphal progress; physical, chemical, biological, medical, and agricultural research work wonders with their aid. Age-old puzzles of the processes of life are solved.

New champions in the battle against disease and death come forward: radio-active iodine throws light on the function and disturbances of the thyroid gland; radio-active sodium enables diseases of the heart and of the circulation to be recognized and traced; radio-active phosphorus permits the exact location of tumours of the brain and simplifies their surgical removal. And radio-active cobalt and cæsium render attainable radiation sources of incredible power—10,000, 100,000, a million curies: radiation equivalent to 10, to 100 kilogrammes, to a ton of radium.

Food is sterilized and preserved by radiation. Trichina are destroyed.

New industries rise on these new foundations. And still pure science presses forward.

New trans-uranic elements are discovered: berkelium and californium, which came to light in 1950, are followed in 1954 by the elements 99 and 100, einsteinium and fermium, in 1955 by mendelevium and in 1957 by nobelium. Thus the atomic number 102 is reached, the hundred elements passed; known atomic weights have risen to 256 from 238, the highest atomic weight occurring naturally being that of uranium.

In the Brookhaven National Laboratory the cosmotron has been completed in 1952, a gigantic proton synchrotron of 80 feet diameter; it produces proton rays with an energy of 2,000 M.e.v. and later of 3,000 M.e.v. Nevertheless, it is overtaken in 1954 by the bevatron in Berkeley, with an initial output of proton rays at 5,000 M.e.v., rising to 6,000 M.e.v.

And—even in Europe—they are aiming yet higher. Here a number of states have united (Germany, after an interval of ten years, is again playing a part in nuclear physics research) to form the CERN, the Conseil Européen pour la Recherche Nucléaire, an association endowed with large resources for atomic research. In Geneva it builds an international Institute and a proton synchrotron of some 480 feet in diameter, designed to reach no less than 25,000 M.e.v.—25 milliard volts! It is scarcely twenty years since as many millions caused a sensation.

But the Americans are not easily outstripped. In Berkeley, the old cyclotron metropolis, they are building an apparatus of the same size. And the Russians are doing likewise.

Meanwhile the machines already in use, the cosmotron and the bevatron, have borne fruit. Not only artificial Pi-mesons and Mu-mesons can be produced by them, but now also heavier mesons and hyperons—the particles which were discovered not long ago in the cosmic rays. Thus opens a new epoch in the experimental study of the unstable elementary particles.

And then, in October 1955, a particle comes to light for which the theorists have long sought: the antiproton, the negative counterpart of the proton, as once the positron, the positive counterpart to the electron, had been found.

The production of pairs and the disappearance of matter in radiation enjoys new triumphs. Limited so far to the electron-positron pair, it now extends to meson pairs and the proton-antiproton pair. An 'anti-material' concept is discernible—the concept of a material in whose atomic nuclei the protons and neutrons are replaced by antiprotons and antineutrons, and the electrons of the shell of the atom by positrons; a material stable in itself, but which needs only to come into contact with ordinary material to break this up and, together with it, to be annihilated in producing non-material energy.

A door is opened upon the vast future potentialities of research.

All the while, however, the atom bombs are blasting, the fire-balls are rising over the Nevada desert, over Eniwetok, over the Siberian plains.

In November 1952 the Americans have followed up the first 'thermonuclear' explosion of May 1951 over the Eniwetok islands with a second, more powerful one. The little island of Elugelab, over which this hell was let loose, disappears from the map of the Pacific, erased by the nucleus which man has liberated.

In August 1953, barely two and a half years after the American hydrogen test, the Russians explode their first H-bomb.

Again there is great agitation in the U.S.A. Russia is on America's heels in the technique of horror; the one spurs on the other.

In February 1954 all is set on Eniwetok for the greatest H-bomb explosion yet seen. It is no longer a 'device', but a proper bomb that could be dropped from an aeroplane. A normal bomb as detonator is surrounded by the hydrogenous material, stable now without supercooling, and the whole has a covering of uranium, whose nuclei will also be split by the neutrons arising from the H-reaction, and so add enormously to the force of the explosion.

On 1st March the great event takes place. Again the bare facts overshadow the calculations: this detonation is twice as powerful as had been reckoned, seven or eight times more powerful than the first American H-test; 700 to 800 times more energy is released than had been by the Hiroshima bomb—fifteen times as much as that of all the bombs dropped on Germany during the war.

An area sixty miles round the point of the explosion has been prohibited to shipping. It is too small. A Japanese fishing-boat with a crew of twenty-three runs into radio-active fall-out some 80 miles from the explosion. Although the boat at once made back to its home port, all the fishermen had already suffered severe damage from radiation.

A wave of horror causes the world to pause and reckon the gravity of the danger that it has brought down upon itself;

another bomb test, calculated to release three times as much energy as before, is abandoned. But the normal bomb tests, with uranium and hydrogen bombs, continue on both sides, in the eastern as well as the western hemisphere.

Terrible refinements are devised. If an H-bomb is encased in cobalt, this, as it evaporates in the moment of the explosion, will be changed into radio-active cobalt, a very strong gamma radiator with a life of over five years. Where this deadly dew settles, life will be no more.

There are people who compute how many dollars it would cost to wipe out life on the earth with hydrogen and cobalt bombs.

*   *   *

When the mushroom of smoke from the atom bomb and its terror have subsided, interest again turns to the peaceful uses of atomic energy.

Here, too, the advance into the atomic age is gathering speed. In 1954 about a dozen nuclear reactors are operating in the United States alone, and elsewhere they are shooting up. Yet experimental reactors are no longer enough: it is time for atomic energy production on an industrial scale.

This is realized in 1954. In June the Russians bring the first power station into service near Moscow: it produces 5,000 kw. of electrical energy with a uranium-fuelled steam plant. At the same time two machines of equivalent output are working in America, the power units for the two planned atom-driven submarines, now on the testing-beds.

On 17th January 1955 the world's first atom-powered ship, the *Nautilus*, starts its trials from the American naval yards at Groton.

Enrico Fermi, builder of the first nuclear reactor, did not see this triumph of atomic energy. A few weeks before, at the age of fifty-three, he died—of cancer! On 18th April he is followed by Albert Einstein, whose solitary voice had admonished the world from Princeton, and whose formula $E = mc^2$ had established the theory of nuclear energy. On 17th March 1956, at the age of fifty-eight, Irène Joliot-Curie will complete the trefoil; the life of the woman whose discovery of artificial radio-activity had so stimulated research, like that of her mother twenty years before, will be ended by radiation.

Meantime plans for bigger power stations are maturing. In America, in Russia, in many smaller countries—particularly Britain—they are taking tangible shape. True, it is still not certain that atomic energy can compete economically with coal and water power. Fuel costs for nuclear power stations are much lower, but the plant costs more. Only a few years ago, this question had been discouraging.

Now there is a new spirit; people decide to act, not to go on waiting. Long before the production of atomic energy can appreciably affect the over-all power situation, the problem of an adequate power supply will have become acute. Future experience will decide whether it is economic; now is the time to act boldly!

And act they do, everywhere.

The Russians build several big power stations of several hundred thousand kilowatts. The Americans build stations at Pittsburg and Shippingport, and Consolidated Edison obtains the concession for a giant power station on the banks of the Hudson, twenty-five miles above New York, which in the near future is to provide a part of the huge city's light and power.

In Britain, large power stations are put up at Calder Hall and at Dounreay. It is planned to derive two million kilowatts of electrical energy from the atomic nucleus in ten years' time, and to change over to nuclear energy for a large part of her power needs in a few decades.

As the atomic scientists pour into Geneva in August 1955 for the big international atomic conference, at which they will exchange their experiences, the gigantic concrete cubes that will house uranium reactors are everywhere springing up, the chimneys that will draw off the cooling gases are rising, the machine-rooms where the electrical generators will soon be humming are being built.

And the conference brings before the public what had been in the background: in the U.S.A., in Britain, in Russia, the scientists and technicians are working to control the 'thermo-nuclear' reaction, to tame the H-bomb. 'Hydrogen instead of uranium' is the motto of the future.

So the broad stream of progress rolls on—into the atomic age.

16

WHAT OF THE FUTURE?

To what future is this ever-broadening stream flowing?
To a future Eden of happiness, or hurtling into the abyss?
Who knows?

A vision is conjured up: the demon nucleus has been tamed,
huge power stations yield the bounty of energy, for which mankind
hungers. Not from uranium; the uranium reactor is already
a museum-piece. Hydrogen provides the energy, from
the harnessing of the fusion reaction. A tiny fraction of the
energy obtained suffices to separate the necessary hydrogen from
the waters of the inexhaustible oceans. The problem of producing
energy has oppressed man for hundreds of years; now it
is solved. There is no more fighting for raw materials, for coal,
for oil. War is something known only from the history books—
there is no reason for it now, there is enough for all. The
nucleus has banished want, an age of harmony has begun on
earth.

Who can tell?

But there is another vision: atomic war has raged over the earth.
Hundreds of H-bombs, of cobalt bombs have fallen on both
sides. Every city is a heap of rubble, hundreds of thousands of
square miles of country are uninhabitable for years to come,
contaminated by radiation. Not even undergrowth will cover
these ruins, as it did those Maya temples—for where the bombs
have ravaged, literally no blade of grass, nothing, will grow; the
ground is a radio-active desert.

There are still people in distant parts, but civilization is
destroyed; production is impossible; the creative elite is obliterated.
Those still scratching a wretched existence can at best

become a new beginning—if they are capable of it: if they do not succumb to the radiation of the radio-active remnants of the many atomic explosions, which menacingly circle the earth as clouds of vapour in the stratosphere.

Who can tell?

And there is yet another vision: the atomic war was avoided, those in authority shrinking from causing utter destruction. An atomic industry has sprung up all over the world; power there is in abundance—but people are not happy, for all that.

Millions of tons of radio-active waste have been buried in the desert and sunk in the sea, sealed in steel containers. But strange subterranean currents have brought these radiating materials back out of the desert in the course of a century; the steel containers, eaten into by the salt water, have released their contents into the sea. And the atmosphere has been poisoned, despite every precaution, by radio-active matter from the stacks of thousands of atomic power stations.

The rain, the snow, every brook, every grain of corn on the stalk, the milk in the cow—everything is contaminated. No one dies from it, but always it is active, generation after generation. And gradually its effect shows: the process of heredity is disturbed, mutations set in; the rate of abortions grows, the number of cripples, of idiots, of bearers of every kind of abnormality rises. Slowly mankind, after an evolution of hundreds of thousands of years, slips into the twilight of a vegetative existence.

Who can dare to say: 'I *know* that it will be thus, and not thus'?

*   *   *

The stream flows on—and it cannot be dammed. Man has ever been compelled by his curiosity to probe nature's secrets; and, almost before he knew it, new power was put in his hands: the control of the forces of nature. But has he really controlled them, or has each new step delivered him further into the power of those natural forces?

Referring to atomic energy, the wise Indian statesman, Pandit Nehru, said: 'The genie from the bottle is overpowering man, who released him.'

In the Oriental tale, the fisherman tricks the genie back into the bottle; but, once they are free, nothing can send the energies of the atomic nucleus back to the sleep in which they rested for milliards of years.

All that remains is to attempt to guide the course of the stream. And how can this be done?

In the political field: remove all old, and avoid all new, tensions; renounce war, which may too easily become an atomic war, as a political means; outlaw any nation which first uses the atomic weapon. Yet the renunciation of all atomic armaments would be sensible only if it were carried out *everywhere* under rigorous supervision. For, sad though it be, a stock of atom bombs on both sides is still a better guarantee of peace than stocks on only one side.

In science: intensified research into the biological, and especially hereditary, dangers of weak radiation, which may threaten from small concentrations of radio-active materials in earth, water, and air. Establishing with absolute reliability the tolerance dosage of radiation.

In atomic engineering: the greatest care in building and running atomic factories and power stations. The sharpest check on the scientifically established safety precautions. A sharp look-out for any radio-active material that might escape. Great care in the disposal of radio-active waste. Safety first!

The programme represents an attempt to direct the stream along its proper course. Only the distant future can decide whether it succeeds.

*　　*　　*

What are the sources of the stream? What are the tributaries that swell it?

One of the strongest reasons for the sudden expansion of the atomic industry is mankind's hunger for energy. It has not always existed: for thousands of years man was content with his own muscles, then with the addition of those of his domestic animals. Later he adds primitive water-wheels, then mills and windmills.

The end of the eighteenth century sees the advent of the giant Steam, bringing the immense Industrial Revolution. A century later comes electrical engineering, the exploitation of water power, the diesel engine. The industrial age rests upon coal, oil, hydraulic power—on energy.

The hunger for energy grows with what it feeds on. The figure for the production of energy rises rapidly: in 1900 the world's consumption of energy (not including losses!) amounted to some 2 billion kw.h.; in 1950 it amounted to above 10 billion kw.h.; in the year 2000 it will be over 80 billion kw.h.

For about a century the world's energy requirements have more or less followed an exponential curve, something we met in the law of radio-active decay. But there it was a falling curve, always halving. In the case of the world's energy needs, it is a rising curve: all the time it doubles.

The Indian sage who asked his master for a chess-board and a grain of corn for the first square, two for the second, four for the third, eight for the fourth, and twice as much for each of the following squares, was demonstrating the results of a rising exponential curve. 1, 2, 4, 8, 16—that looks harmless enough. For the eighth square, at the end of the first line, there are 128 grains; by the sixteenth there are 32,768—about two pounds of corn. And then the flood starts: at the end of the third row come 7 cwt., at the end of the fourth 85 tons. This has provided half the chess-board with its corn. Then comes the torrent. At the end of the fifth row come 22,000 tons, at the end of the sixth 6 million tons—more than a year's production of corn in Germany. The end of the seventh row demands $1\frac{1}{2}$ milliard tons; and the last square, the sixty-fourth, claims by itself over 9 trillion grains, about one third of a billion tons of corn: far more than the total world production since the beginnings of grain cultivation in prehistoric times.

That is the exponential curve; and it has a disquieting effect. It expresses the fact that things cannot go on like this: it is the sign of an acute crisis.

And so the exponential curve of the world's energy requirements represents an acute crisis.

But behind this is another, still more menacing exponential curve: that of the increase in the population of the world.

Here we see a terrifying parallel. Down to the eighteenth century the human race grew comparatively slowly; then it rose sharply, and ever since has followed almost exactly an exponential curve.

A rising exponential curve showing doubling in about a century. In 1800 the earth had 900 million inhabitants; in 1850 it had 1,200 million; in 1900 1,600 million. In 1950 the population figure has risen to nearly 2,500 million. The curve rises!

Doubling in every hundred years means increasing a thousandfold every thousand years.

No one will believe that the earth can ever support 3 billion people instead of 3 milliard, or, after a further thousand years, 3,000 billion people. The exponential curve rises *ad absurdum*. The crisis of man's development is also acute. But such a crisis is measured in centuries, not in years. To-day we are at its beginning. What will its future bring?

Into this dangerous age of rising exponential curves, of hectic industrial and scientific development, comes atomic energy; and in this context it must be seen. Is it not the obvious expression of the modern age, with its boundless potentialities? A necessary and appropriate element in a time of explosive expansion in every direction?

History—in its broadest sense—is made by man. Yet it is impossible not to feel that man faces his own historical evolution as helplessly as if it were some extraneous natural force.

For a hundred years the world has been shaken in its foundations.

But it is not *only* the scientists who have shaken it, with their probing of the demonic forces of nature, leading finally to the unleashing of untold power.

The beacon of our age that shows the way into the future at once most brilliantly and most menacingly is the liberation of the dormant nucleus, the attempt to snatch the sun's fire.

It all began in that February of the year 1896, with an unimpressive, supposedly fluorescent radiation from uranium compounds.